WE NEUROTICS

WE NEUROTICS

FRESNO, CALIFORN

Handbook for the Half-mad

ERNARD BASSET, S. J.

DEMY GUILD PRESS

Library of Congress Catalog Card Number: 63-12102

First printing

LITHOGRAPHED AND BOUND IN THE UNITED STATES OF
AMERICA BY THE NORTH CENTRAL PUBLISHING
COMPANY OF SAINT PAUL, MINNESOTA

CONTENTS

FOREWORD

THIS is an unusual book, part fact, part fiction and, as the title suggests, not meant for all.

Need it be stressed that the characters are entirely fictitious, all place names accidental, all situations contrived. Yet the lessons here set out were once acquired, are valid and may be verified. The book is rather more than fiction as those will discover who pray lying on the ground.

Friends who kindly checked the script reacted with vigour, some whispering words like "facetious", "flippant", "superficial", others asserting that they were very much helped. There are obvious problems when writing in the first person about someone other than oneself. The point of view is restricted and the author is saddled with mannerisms, aversions, expressions which he himself would not normally accept. Yet, on so sacred and urgent a subject, there is much to be said for the setting which brings sublime truth down to the level on which so many have to live. Thus a doctor who was losing her eye-sight, a nun recovering from a serious operation, a married man overwhelmed with worries seemed helped by this form of presentation and afforded an excuse to go ahead. Despite the laughter, this book is in deadly earnest and it would be sad if any of the well-intentioned chatter gave any personal offence.

A book with so unfortunate a title may, scarcely, be offered to one's friends. Sufficient to express my thanks to Fr Austin Delaney, O.S.B., and to Jean and Alan Hillgarth whose kindness allowed me to finish by the quiet waters of the Shannon what had been started in the delightful, Cornish setting of St Ives.

1

ENTER THE LITTLE NUN

DESPITE an alarming title, this is a soothing book. Amateurish and inconsequential, it matches the moods of the solitary pilgrim who set out from a London suburb to find peace of soul. The incidents are trivial and their movement slow. Its only merit is its indiscretion for it treats of subjects rarely mentioned by the wise and prudent who are far too anxious not to give themselves away. Let it be dedicated to those thousands of charming people, shopping quite normally at Marks and Spencers, who, in their bathrooms and bedrooms, know themselves to be a little mad.

One thinks of that parish priest in London, a lion in the pulpit, who would walk for a quarter of a mile in the wrong direction rather than pass a dog in the street. There were, too, those unmarried sisters, living outside Preston, who, every night, trembled alternately as one or other thought that she could hear a man on the stairs. Where is poor Maisie now, Maisie who could eat a steak for dinner but could not be persuaded by the doctors to swallow even the smallest pill? Jean, most expert of Fleet Street typists, used to come over queer of an evening and could scarcely breathe in the home-going train. George, in the same rush-hour panic, found the urge towards suicide alarming but this extreme temptation only hit him if he travelled by the Bakerloo. Last of all comes Dan, up with me at Oxford in the twenties, who so fretted about his lack of inches that he would spend a full half-hour every morning placing strips of corrugated paper in his shoes. Misery faces those who find in themselves such symptoms; hope is re-born in the further, unkind discovery that thousands of others are walking on their own kind of corrugated paper, too.

I visited an asylum some weeks ago—not as a patient—and saw there the sublime happiness of the completely mad. Queenie came in while I was taking tea with matron and she, believing herself to belong to one of the last of the ruling families of Europe, had enjoyed for the past thirty years a gay and exuberant life. Hearing that I came from London, she drew herself to her full height. She presumed, she said, that I came from David's side of the family, and if I was calling at Clarence House, would I tell Margaret that she had been photographed with her baby on the wrong arm. I agreed, of course, pondering on the lunatic's blissful lot. We poor neurotics never escape from ourselves. Queenie was contented; she cast no furtive glances in my direction to see if I had noted her defect. She believed that she was a Queen and rested happy in the thought. I had to return home to struggle with a thousand, pitiful panics and pretences hidden behind a middle-class façade.

On this one subject Margery is of little use. Of sterling yeoman stock, reared in the country, schooled at a high-class convent, Margery's armour has no chinks. In her childhood it was reckoned very, very vulgar to faint. Smelling salts were the short term cure followed by Senna Pods or a good hiding until fresh air and exercise could produce a stabilising effect. Far be it from me to deny the efficacy of such treatment which has made Margery, in the early fifties, almost painfully sane. To mix metaphors across the Atlantic, she has crossed to Madison Avenue from Harley Street. Diet is for Margery what scruples are to me. She is always fit, healthy, outgiving, radiant but with an appalling price to pay. Nasal sprays, wholemeal bread, toothpaste which cleans, sterilizes and lubricates provide poor consolation to a middle-aged man consumed with fear. Margery says her grace before meals and then balances proteins against carbohydrates as though there was no God in heaven at all.

Are calory fiends in their own small way a little mad? I once knew a wonderful man, an alcoholic, who, after bringing his wife and children to destitution, cured himself by grace and determination after making a spiritual retreat. I myself proposed this retreat and the priest who arranged it was so delighted that he gave three cheers for the Holy Ghost. Mr Owles was cured, he joined the Alcoholics Anonymous, a wonderful body, and has gone no further than a glass of

Horlicks since that day. But, sickening thought, the
Alcoholics Anonymous have taken the place of drink
for him. He lives, dreams and talks of nothing else. I
would have him on the phone each day for twenty
minutes, mouthing statistics, citing cases, hatching
plans. Eventually I remarked, half-fooling, that if he
went on much longer I would be taking to the bottle
myself. I heard a despairing gasp at the other end of
the line. "Hold on, old man," he whispered. "Do nothing foolish; within forty minutes I'll have one of my
best contacts around!"

Who am I to mock at Margery or at Mr Owles? I do
not know how this limited lunacy takes you; for me
the symptoms of neurosis have been legion, swallow-
ing, blinking, scruples, drink, suicide, mysticism, murder, lack of confidence, over confidence, fear of cancer,
death and God. I have consulted doctors galore and
could once boast a cupboard in the bathroom jammed
with sedatives. Strange how one rarely takes them, for
once a doctor has reassured you, you no longer need
his pills.

Once, a kind friend recommended a visit to a skilled
psychiatrist; I agreed but never went. Neurotics respect the "know how" of the expert while shying at
treatment for themselves. Margery and her school
think psychology a bad word and know no symptoms
which Ovaltine and Holy Water cannot cure. I
shunned treatment for a deeper reason; I knew that I
was shamming, that if our house caught fire I would
soon forget my symptoms in the smoke. This, alas, is a

costly type of cure. We neurotics are dishonest, we lack the determination to free ourselves. Miserable we are and frightened, beyond the reach of others, so deceitful that we even fool ourselves.

I owed my cure not to psychiatrists or Margery but to the calm advice of a quaint little nun. She was short, stout, deaf and famous—matron of a hospital for backward children—she had the twinkle of Mr Pickwick and the features of the more pleasant type of county court judge. Another endearing trait, she placed her hand on your sleeve during conversation for she was very hard of hearing and this contact helped to master the defect. We first met twenty years ago and I found myself in the embarrassing situation of sitting in a public lecture hall in Cheadle with a little nun holding my arm.

It is difficult to remember all the details but I know that I was feeling very ill. I had left home that morning secretly convinced that I had stomach ulcers which would, at any moment, burst. I was also secretly ashamed that so promising a young man with bowler hat and brief-case could be such a fool. The ulcers vanished as the train drew out of Euston, swamped in the greater panic that the express might leave the rails. I made acts of contrition all the way from Watford to Nuneaton and as we crashed through that not very inspiring township, I could stand it no longer and rose to pull the communication cord. The stolid party opposite smiled sweetly at me, remarking that it was disgraceful the way the railways wasted time.

Expresses took so long that she often wondered if they would ever get there and I, wondering the same but for other reasons, promptly sat down.

I reached Manchester a wreck. Muttering to myself and with eyes moist with self-pity and humiliation, I recall that I bought a bottle of a patent nerve tonic and swallowed a thumping dose as soon as I had reached the hotel. As the last drops trickled down my throat, my eye noticed the grim warning on the bottle: "It is dangerous to exceed the stated dose". I fled to the hall before the first paroxysms could begin and revealed my plight to the hotel porter who decided that as I was not yet a corpse, this was hardly a case for the police. He gave me the number of a local doctor who answered the phone in a flat, unemotional tone. When he heard the name of the tonic he remarked drily: "That muck; six bottles of it would scarcely bring a faint blush to a maiden's cheek."

I survived the long night and arrived, spruced up, for my lecture the next morning at half past ten. I looked calm, certainly knew my subject, secretly was on the very edge of tears.

The lecture went well. I was speaking about history text-books for backward children with a great many teachers in the audience.

The Little Nun popped up from nowhere as question time merged with coffee break. Dedicated men and women were standing about, discussing my facts and exchanging sheaves of duplicated paper when I suddenly felt a persistent tapping on my arm. I turned round to see her smiling up at me. She pointed to the window seat, explained her deafness, chuckled as she took my arm. "It is a good thing that they know me here," she remarked smiling. "I can guess what John Knox would have said."

She congratulated me on my lecture and, presumably, asked me a question or two. I recall that she scribbled my answers on an old envelope. I also remember how she remarked with a quaint, old fashioned grace that there was no need for me to raise my voice in speaking, provided that I moved my lips. Thus started a profound friendship with a series of embarrassing grimaces as I laboriously turned the conversation towards myself.

Do not ask me why I confided in a total stranger, somehow I trusted her face. Sufficiently depressed, you come around to your worries very swiftly, sufficiently holy, you appear to be interested even if stone deaf. The Little Nun had the indefinable grace of smiling without laughing and of permitting me to wrap up in the third person problems which she knew pertained to myself.

Pulling faces, I was forced to speak slowly; she spoke much faster but with very long pauses in which she arranged her thoughts. She spoke gently with an old world manner which in no way lessened her alertness and authority.

"Mr Dawes," she said, "if you had had the time to visit my clinic and to study the nervous problems of little children, you would be less surprised to find that so many adults are, what I think they call, a little 'cracked'. Please remember that human beings are all very different. Doctors may lump us all together for bodily complaints, for kidneys, rheumatism, blood tests, for, thank goodness, we all have the same kind of organs in more or less the same kind of place. But when it comes to the soul and to its contact with the body, we are all very different and each individual must spend his whole life adjusting himself."

Her deafness accounted for two unconscious mannerisms, she would breathe deeply and make a faint click with her lips. While I spoke, she was watching intently and would tap with her fingers in quick succession on my wrist. Such was her skill that within a few minutes one quite forgot that she was deaf.

"Have you," she asked, "ever taken part in a personality test? You have not—I am very sorry about that. The results are invariably fascinating and would have helped you to grasp the point which I am trying to make. Only yesterday, I showed the same ink smudge to five intelligent people and had five completely different replies. One saw the smudge as an X-ray of a kidney, the second thought that it might be the coast of New Guinea, a third, the marshalling yards at Ham. I do not recall the other two but they were unlike." She smiled. "I can see that you have not yet grasped my point; it is simply this, that we are all so very, very different in originality, determination, perseverance, imagination, sensitive response. We have different backgrounds, varying associations, shifting shades of anticipation, and while doctors may help us in organic cases, most normal people must struggle for integration by themselves."

She darted a penetrating glance in my direction. "I was going to quote Freud," she said, "but I don't think I will.

"The fact to remember is that we are all abnormal; it would be very, very distressing if we ever met any-one exactly like ourselves. It is for this reason that we all feel loneliness, all fear that we are unusual, fear that others will guess our secrets and are looking at us. It is a false fear. Everyone in secret passes through these periods of tension and as each one only knows himself, he surrenders to self-pity instead of recognis-ing that such tension is normal, part of the struggle to become a true man. I put it all in the masculine," she said with a wink, "because I am a woman and every-one knows that women are neurotic anyway."

She winked again and waved to two passing blue-stockings but without releasing the grip on my arm. "I am over sixty now," she said, "and have grown in wisdom but I can well remember trembling, weeping, screaming my head off even as a nun; what makes it worse is that a deaf nun in such a crisis is heard very far away."

She sat back relaxed and gazed kindly at me, search-ing my face to see if the lesson had gone home. "Do not be afraid to speak," said she, tapping my sleeve with her finger; "if I cannot follow every word, I can have a good guess."

So I told her all my woes, of my failure to find a solution, of my fear that I would end in a mental home. The audience was returning from its coffee and one or two cast a casual glance in our direction, possibly supposing that I was helping the Little Nun. She, dear soul, raised a hand in salute but without taking her eyes from my lips. She may have missed a word or two but she certainly heard my final remark for she breathed loud in irritation when I supposed that she, like all the others, would exhort me to bear my cross, take plenty of milk and pray.

She slapped her lips together in disapproval and gave an extra tug to my sleeve. "My dear Mr Dawes," said she, "prayer is really no good at all in such a situation, indeed in many cases it does positive harm. By all means have a general intention of accepting God's decisions but after that pretend to be an atheist for a couple of weeks. Praying about your troubles is but a subtle way of thinking of yourself."

Again she sat back primly like Queen Victoria in a statue and, for a moment, placed both hands in her lap. Within three seconds she was again perched on my wrist. "No, the only hope for you is relaxation. If you really want to right yourself, I will show you how. Probably it will all be a waste of time because so few neurotics are willing to adopt these simple methods or are humble enough to do more than talk about themselves." A sharp, beady little eye darted forward to underline this point. She stopped to rummage in a battered leather bag. "I always carry with me," she said, puffing slightly, "a copy of this very helpful little book. It was written by two doctors and has the title *Relaxation in Everyday Life*. It is a simple book to read and I will lend it to you if you will promise most seriously to read it to the final page."

Again she gave her delightful little chuckle. "I have to extract such a promise because my copies are so precious and I cannot have them lying about unread. This one, I see, really belongs to the Warrington Health Committee but they won't be minding lending it to a suffering Southerner. Read it carefully in the train on your way back to London; if you want to be cured, have the courage to follow its advice."

She handed over the modest little book, first flicking through the pages to remove small bits of paper covered with scribbled notes. The audience was now re-assembling for my second lecture but the Little Nun would not release me without a final word.

"Mr Dawes," she said, solemnly and slowly, "you are but one among thousands in this very city who face the problem of curing themselves. We talk of people finding their feet, a ridiculous expression; the real task for most people is to find their souls. First step, you must learn to relax. And when I use the word 'relax', I am, of course referring to therapeutic relaxation; from what you have told me this might be a very useful word for your wife.

"Do not pray for, perhaps, a month, for God Himself is not at His best till we are relaxed. Just as I cannot help my children at the clinic until they are mus-

cularly peaceful, so God needs a similar condition in
the spiritual life. Dear Mr Dawes, be warned in time.
By relaxation most people mean sitting in an easy
chair, chain smoking and listening to a thriller on the
radio. Some of the books which people read on holiday are enough to send them to an establishment.
There is nothing therapeutic in distractions of this
kind. You are a clever man and you have read of the
Eastern mystics and their methods of prayer. My cure
will end up as a Christian version of that. Mr Dawes,
I must repeat that you are on the edge of a great discovery and I must ask you to send the book back."

The Little Nun rose with a Victorian grace, thanked
me for my lecture, collected her battered bag, smiled
and hurried away.

So great was her influence that I studied her book
carefully on the long journey back to London and the
express reached Euston without a single suggestion
that it might leave the rails. I gathered that I must
lie on the floor for forty minutes daily with one low
pillow to ease the strain on the neck. The authors
warned me that it would probably take as long as a
month to learn to relax. I must start seriously with my
toes, my knees, my ankles and so work slowly up the
body letting each muscle go. So absorbed was I that
I kicked the passenger opposite; it was clear that he
could do with a course of relaxation too.

Our authors were particularly worried about the
chest. It seems that this section always proves refrac-
tory and must be persuaded to let go. They suggested

the cunning device of picturing the chest as covered by a football jersey of many horizontal stripes. The colours of these stripes were to be the colours of the spectrum and these were set out in a diagram. One had to concentrate on one particular colour, say green or orange, and at once the corresponding part of the chest would relax. The beady eye of the Little Nun, now two hundred miles away in Cheadle, was still strong enough to make me take the authors seriously. When at last the whole body was at rest, I had to stretch out my arms as a cat does so that the claws are exposed. Then with my arms loose on my chest and my feet crossed for polarisation, I was to lie quite still for forty minutes, seeing myself strolling leisurely through luscious, green fields.

Margery was deeply impressed by the word "therapeutic" and pleased that I had been speaking to a nun. She, however, took the line that no real man in his senses would lie on the floor with his face upwards unless he was dead. Harry and Benjamin, aged nine and eight, took the whole exercise more seriously and I was solemnly escorted to the bedroom with a pillow carried before me in state. Margery insisted on a clean pillow-case.

I had been crazy enough before and felt very much worse at each therapeutic session but I have to admit, looking back, that the Little Nun was right. I followed her in everything, even pretending to be an atheist. After making the intention that God's will should be done, I followed the instructions, lying on the carpet, my feet crossed like some dead crusader and with the colours of the spectrum round my chest.

After three weeks without a break, I could relax with comfort and the luscious green fields arrived at once. I was even tempted to exceed the stated dose. There were times when I wanted to stay recumbent for ever and days when I thought that I was paralysed for good. The colours of the spectrum did their bit and with deeper and deeper breathing came the strange sensation of living in a trance. One was pleased to be mad, free to float away for forty minutes, to recline in a meadow clear of insects, barred to cows.

Margery nearly ruined it all by saying that soon I would be unbalanced, that even at the moment she reckoned me every bit as odd as Mr Owles. Her suggestion was alarming, was the very cure a sign that I was mad?

In this moment of crisis the boys took a hand. Through the bedroom door I could hear them whispering in the hall below.

"Bet you he'll let us," said Harry.

"Bet you he won't," answered Benjamin.

"How much will you bet?" asked Harry. "He always says Yes when he has been lying on the floor."

When I returned the book to the Little Nun, I added in a postscript that the cure was working but that I was getting a little bored with the luscious green fields.

Came the cryptic reply, written in purple ink on a

postcard: "If you are an agnostic, then, luscious green fields will have to suffice. If you are a believer, now is the time to edge forward a little further but do go very slowly and remain lying down."

2

MISS COPSLEY-SMITH EXPLAINS

NOTHING that I can say, dear reader, will persuade you to relax on the floor. The cure is too extreme, too cold, too humiliating to commend itself to anyone as sane as you. Twenty years ago and in deep distress, I managed to maintain the practice only for a month. Since then I have used it on occasion and have evolved a diluted version in an easy chair.

The Little Nun was right, however, for relaxation in our present era is an acquired taste. Babies relax but children lose the aptitude almost as soon as they see a TV screen. We grown-ups pretend to relax but our very entertainments are often more nervously exhausting than our work. I have watched colleagues, who took up golf for relaxation, reach the 18th green with more agony and tension than auxiliary firefighters in the London blitz.

Whether we lie on the floor or sit in a chair, the therapeutic value of relaxation proves so dynamic that, unaided by pills and prescriptions, it more than doubles our capacity for life. If, too, we are happy

16

enough to believe in a future life beyond this one, the same relaxation is essential in the progress of the soul towards God. It may seem odd that muscular tension impedes spiritual effort but the Little Nun was right in her contention that God is not at His best while we are tense. Bird lovers will know how impossible it is to strike up a friendship with budgerigars who are in a flap.

For me the hours on the floor led to the further discovery that luscious green fields are not enough. Green is certainly a soothing colour with unending appeal to the suburban dweller, robbed of his heritage. Green fields, however, soon grow boring while the deeper forms of worry build up resistance to so mild a drug.

Lying relaxed and breathing deeply, one is carried to the very frontier of an uncharted land. Wordsworth, lying on the floor, might have found daffodils sufficient, though I doubt it; Shakespeare, in the same relaxed position, would have found it impossible to stop. We are not all Shakespeares but our horizon is eternal for our souls were made to the image and likeness of God. Considered vertically such a statement is cold but credible; try it horizontally, lying on your back. I certainly was aware of the need to go further; the purple-inked card from the Little Nun was for me a green light.

What step to take next? One badly needs help to avoid delusions but where to get it and how limit it to plain advice? To each man his own system and if you ask him for his opinion he at once becomes a commercial traveller and sets out to sell you a line. So Mrs Ponsonby is all for Lourdes; I escaped with a life of St Bernadette, a jar of water from the grotto and a plastic madonna which glowed at night. Father Mulligatawny, the curate, knew nothing of relaxation but could quote every papal pronouncement about industrial unrest. The lady in the flower shop was hot on the nine first Fridays and also gave me a leaflet on the Holy Shroud of Turin. I was reminded in all this of the duplicator in our office which one day decided not to work. A subordinate was asked to see a man about it with calamitous results. We found ourselves committed to a brand new model with special ink, paper and stencils which could only be replaced or serviced by a special firm. This may also happen to you in prayer. You seek advice and you will be lucky to escape without a monthly newsletter, two patrons, three novenas and a subscription to a missionary magazine.

Prayer, as we know, is a delicate subject, deeply personal, in which each must find his own approach. It is all very well to crib a few lines from St Alphonsus or the prophet Daniel but, somehow, our aspirations must be our own. Lying on the floor, I felt that there must be a neurotic form of prayer for neurotic people and a prayer of relaxation for those who seek supernatural peace.

Up from the floor and tingling with spiritual excitement, I naturally turned to Margery first. Long before

I had proposed to her, Margery and I had teased each other about prayer. Margery's spiritual life is organised and orderly; she could almost put God wise about His prerogatives after she has consulted one of her many little books. Margery has an Italian saint up her sleeve to suit any occasion and a prayerbook to match any mood. Her prayers, as I have often told her, lie halfway between an insurance policy and a police report; prayers for those who want a good harvest, a safe journey, a vocation or a happy delivery; prayers for those who have incurred a censure, committed adultery or are awaiting a summons from the Eternal Judge.

"I have told you already," said Margery, "that lying on the floor is doing you no good. You have had two heavy colds in three weeks and we'll be having the neighbours talking next. Don't say later that I did not warn you; lie on the floor much longer and you'll be developing a religious vocation, asking me to enter a convent so that you may become a monk. Well, I'm going to start a novena to St Philibert of Bologna for your recovery; in case you do not know, he is the patron saint of women with imaginary pregnancies!" Margery speaks like that on occasion; this time she wagged her head sideways and put out her tongue.

The Canon, who knew us both before our marriage, smiled when I told him about this. A fine old man, tall, slightly stooped, very liturgical, he is able to laugh at his own foibles and looks a little like Cardinal Manning after a good meal. He is a stickler for rubrics, fussy about ceremonial details, not demonstrative in prayer. Once, when he had insisted on a rubrical nicety to the annoyance of the sacristan, he turned to me conspiratorially: "Henry," he said in a stage whisper, "I am a little worried. When I go to Rome, I find that they know very little about Westminster and, maybe, when I get to heaven, I will find that they do not follow Fortescue and O'Connell there. Pray what will happen to me then?"

I knew that the Canon was not in sympathy with Margery's devotions but would he approve of praying on the floor? He puckered his brow and thought for a while. "We do lie down," he said, "on Good Friday and Holy Saturday but only for a few minutes and never on our backs. It would be far more liturgical to turn the other way round." Beyond that he would not go and he made the point with repeated emphasis that the liturgy is not concerned with nerves. "That is the beauty of it," he said. "It is not concerned with man and his tantrums, it directs his eye to the public service of God. Those who follow the official prayers of the Church take their minds off themselves. Just occasionally we say a few words for people like yourself as in the psalm at the foot of the altar, '*Quare tristis es anima mea et quare conturbas me?*' Otherwise, the liturgy is not much interested in madmen though, I admit, some liturgists grow a little odd."

The Canon may not have helped very much but he it was who offered a solution when he said on parting, "If you want esoteric devotion, why not have a

word with dear Miss Copsley-Smith?" His face was
serious as he said this but I saw a very unliturgical
twinkle in his eye.

Miss Copsley-Smith was a figure of fun in our home.
A vigorous, middle-aged woman, almost ugly, her
complexion was one shade lighter than her fawn
coloured shoes. Everyone knew that she was smartly
connected, that one half of her hyphen had descended
from the English martyrs while the other half had
made its money in oil. A Mayfair monsignor took tea
in her house and called her Gertrude and our boys
had, somehow, found this out. They, too, referred to
her as Gertrude and liked to imitate her abrupt manner
and moorland gait. They had wickedly observed that
she liked to be first or last at the Communion rail on
Sunday and, in the blasphemous style of adolescents,
spent half the Mass working to thwart her plan. When
Margery had warned me, I soon put a stop to all that.

Miss Copsley-Smith had a delightful little flat just
off the High Street, a flat which was half antique shop
and half slum. If it was the Copsley furniture which
made it—I am only guessing—then it must have been
from the Smith side of the family that she drew her
talent and eccentricity. Miss Copsley-Smith was not
only gifted but brave enough to put her hand to anything. One day she would be painting, next metal
beating and then, of a sudden, she would vanish for
three months. The boys announced that she had told
them that she was off to run a youth hostel on the
Italian coast. Wherever she had been, she returned in

a bright blue sports car acquired from a Copsley cousin who had entered a Greek monastery, Uniate, of course.

From time to time Miss Copsley-Smith would invite us to dinner at her flat. It was a bewildering experience and I would never allow the children to come. She always served cocktails but, invariably, lacked either vermouth or gin. Once when the former was missing, she insisted that we follow the old Greek custom of taking gin with sour milk.

A superb continental cook, she loved to experiment. Should she decide that it would be far more cosy to eat in the kitchen, one had to watch out for paint or metal filings in the meat. Once we had a Dalmatian Duck cooked with its head on, once an enormous cod's roe in a kind of plastic sponge-bag, once the stove blew up because modelling clay had blocked the exhaust.

An enormous Madonna, made by Miss Copsley-Smith herself from sea shells and jasper, dominated the drawing-room mantelpiece. Next to Our Lady was a Georgian decanter, labelled Sherry, but Miss Copsley-Smith always had to smell it to discover whether it held sherry, port or turps. With her you never knew what would happen next. Once, not long before my present visit, she phoned one morning to ask if anyone wanted a bath. She roared with laughter when I mistook her meaning and then explained that she had acquired a glorious blue enamel bath from a cousin who had gone off to be a Carmelite nun. If we wanted the bath, we must come at once to fetch it as it blocked the entire passage and she could not reach her bedroom door. Two days later I was asked to buy shares in a small factory that she had purchased for making patent ashtrays for aeroplanes. They were—need I add—of her own invention and brilliantly contrived.

A few years ago when Miss Copsley-Smith took sick, few people worried about her; when she died in a London hospital, three days later, she left an un-bridgeable gap. She was certainly unusual but the Canon was one with me in wondering whether, in her own weird way, she was not a saint.

On the particular evening in question, my call was connected with the blue enamel bath. A vital part was missing and we found it in her kitchen serving as an improvised stand for a dirty brush. Readily I took the invitation to stay on for a drink.

It would be impossible to imitate her style, the sudden asides, the way she would dart off on to irrele-vant topics without changing the main subject or los-ing the thread. Verbs with her were few and redundant, her eyebrows took their place. Yet ten minutes with her could be far more scarifying than a standard sermon twice as long. For me, at least, the doctrine which she proposed that evening served as a lighthouse over many years.

She was, I remember, delighted with the wisdom of the Little Nun. As for relaxing on the floor, she had learned the trick in India as a little girl. "That is why

I am so tranquil and relaxed," she solemnly asserted before darting off to arrange a bowl of dried flowers with such masculine vigour that most of the poor, withered blossoms fell in powder on the floor. "Can't be helped," she said, kicking them petulantly. "I told Nan not to bring them; I do not like them as they remind me of cemeteries in France."

When, undaunted by all this, I moved on to the prayer of relaxation, Miss Copsley-Smith became much more quiet and sat down in an easy chair with a bang. "Let us hope it is only the spring," she remarked without looking. "One of the Copsley cousins was in hospital for over three months."

It took her some time to settle even after we had started talking about prayer. One of the bangles on her arm showed signs of misbehaving; it was off in a moment and she was biting one of the links with her teeth. "Now," she said, replacing the bangle, patting it, squinting at it sideways, "what are you fussing about?"

So we started all over again. "Surely," she asked, "you know all about the three layers in prayer? Teresa of Avila may have put it better but, sorry, they remain three layers to me. When I think about prayer, I am reminded of those little men in the nursery who fitted one inside the other in a most ingenious way. One thing is very certain that we are not as simple as so many writers like to suppose. Talk about split personalities, most of us are treble, faint replicas of Father, Son and Holy Ghost.

"Now, more about these layers for they are very, very important if ever we are to understand ourselves. The first Me is myself in public as people see me, the Me which may be checked at the customs by a snapshot and those silly details which we have to supply on our passport forms. I am thirteen stone, four; five-foot, five inches high, brown eyes, slightly crooked, and with a mole on the lower cheek. That is the Me that everybody knows, and because we live our lives in public we are, on this layer, actors and actresses. Shakespeare said as much in better language, but frankly, I sometimes find the bard a bit of a bore. Anyhow, in public there we all are, playing our parts with a script in our hands. Some of us are comedians, some smart, some sexy, many cynical. I am eccentric, the Canon liturgical, you, heaven knows what."

She paused to kick the fire with her shoe. "The second Me," she said, "is in my bedroom when I am alone. There is no audience now. I am like an actress back in the greenroom and parting with both paint and props. No applause now, no audience, no reputation, no conventions, no part to play in your room." She laughed hilariously for a moment and was suddenly solemn again. "Help," she said. "What odd things people do in their rooms. I have seen things, I can tell you; I was a Red-Cross nurse in the first war.

"Do you know," she said, all of a sudden, quiet, "some people are Christians in public and atheists in their rooms. And I have seen it the other way round, too. People play games with themselves, argue in the mirror, look for lumps in their neck which they think might be cancer, read dirty novels covered with brown paper, cry over old letters, write anonymous letters, juggle with the soap. Do you remember what fun it was as a youngster when you were ill enough to be kept in bed? They would bring a tray with a napkin and many little dishes but I used to say to myself in my second layer: 'Gertrude, old girl, I'm hanged if you're going to be a lady once they are out of the room.'

"The third layer, the deepest level of Me, takes much more finding and is far further down. Teresa of Avila located it in the head; Spinoza thought it was in the pancreas; the Church has not spoken, so, Mr Dawes, you may take your choice. Personally I identify it with the heart—not this great turnip of an organ which develops coronaries but that dark, uncharted place deep down inside us from which all our desires, motives, ambitions spring. Neurosis starts there too. I wish that the psalmist had been a little more explicit, a little less vulgar; when he speaks about reins and bowels, he is really trying to say the same thing."

Miss Copsley-Smith turned suddenly and stared fiercely at me. "Christ," she said, "put the whole problem in a nutshell. He said, 'It is from the overflow of the heart that the mouth speaks,' and, 'Where your treasure is, your heart will be.' My dear Mr Dawes, if you lie on the floor and solve these two quotations, you should, if there is any justice, become the first lay Doctor of the Church."

She jumped to her feet. "While you are hunting for the third Me, I am off to make some coffee; it should be ready in a moment. I had it boiling at least two hours ago."

She returned in a second to announce that it was not boiling, that some fool without thinking had turned down the gas. She remained leaning on the door. "Go home, Mr Dawes," she said, "and lie on the floor by all means, but if you do not find the third Me and get to know it, you will certainly be wasting your time." She gave the kind of chuckle that a horse would recognise. "The Canon," she said, "thinks that I am crazy but I remind him not to be too certain of the liturgy for Annas and Caiphas were liturgists with empty hearts."

She had gone again, this time for slightly longer, and when she returned she carried a tray. She slapped it down on the little centre table, slightly listing to port. In transit, she kicked the pouffe to the other side of the room.

"Mr Dawes," she remarked with an old fashioned bow. "You may have noticed that I myself am slightly odd. This may be due to the Copsley connection for many of our older families have, over the centuries, turned a little quaint. I prefer to think that it comes from living alone. My outside layer is not fully developed as I so rarely play before an audience. But solitude has its compensations and I know a good deal about my own heart. Now, for the love of the Lord, stop talking and pour yourself out some coffee; what is more you must help me to finish this frightful bottle of port. Nan brought it and if I heard her rightly, she bought it for a few shillings in a low down Cypriot store."

She also took some port but before she had sipped it, she was standing above me labouring her point. "Go home," she cried. "Relax your muscles and then start the thrilling journey to the centre of your soul. Teresa preferred to see herself climbing upwards, so did St John of the Cross. I go downwards as I am a bit too old to change even for them. Get to know the Me in public, playing its elected part. Shake hands with the Me in private, so much less a humbug, pacing up and down the room when the door is shut. Then, further down still to the person who has been talking to himself since the age of four. Where is that little voice? Find the capital I with whom you have been having a ceaseless conversation for so long. You are in a world without feeling, a world in which your eyes and ears do not function; a world which has eyes and ears and a sensitive system of its own. If you are honest and I think you are, you will admit that, in the very centre of yourself, there is a great longing, a yearning which is never satisfied. You long for what?"

She answered her own question, using me almost as a ventriloquist's doll. "When you were young," she said, "you yearned for toffee, for Christmas and birthday presents, for red jelly with a dab of cream. Later it was girls, sex, money, reputation, summer holidays abroad. You are still longing but now what you want is a decent pension, an understanding dentist and for Margery to outlive your old age. The psalmist describes our soul as a hart panting after water; as we see so very few harts in modern London, I prefer to learn my lesson from the dogs. Whenever I see a dog padding along with its tongue on the pavement, I say to myself: "Gertrude Copsley-Smith, your soul is like that, Ha Ha!"

She was so busy laughing at herself that I could get a word in, told her of the sense of elation when one was relaxing and asked her to explain the next step.

"The next step?" she queried, puzzled and scratching her head with her coffee spoon. After staring at the fire for a moment, she turned towards me again. "Let me put it this way. Do you know those little cardboard models of the human body used by doctors and nurses in their student days? You have a flat little cardboard man with no clothes on so that the students may study his superficial structure, skin, joints and veins. You put the little fellow flat on his back and you open up his first little flaps. Up with the skin and the ribs and you come to the various organs, starting with the lungs. Up with the lungs and you come to the heart, up with the heart and you find the liver, up with the liver and all the tubing and eventually you come to his spine. Admittedly it is not very elegant but that is how I pray. I open myself up layer by layer, starting with myself on the surface, my

eccentricities, my metal beating, my Margaret Ruther-
ford approach. Next, I come down to myself in my
room when no one is looking, my games, my fears,
my vanity, the fact that I never married, my sorrow,
my remorse. Open up that and I arrive at the Ego or
what I would prefer to call the heart. Lift up the flaps
and I uncover the central longing, this yearning, this
desire and I invite God to look in and to fill it up. I sit
or lie down and being very liturgical, though the
Canon does not think so, I say inside: "Take a peep
O Lord."

She stopped abruptly, highly embarrassed,
snatched away my coffee cup before I had finished
and announced that she would not detain me any
more.

I was for letting it pass. It took courage to put the
next question but I felt that I might never have
another chance. "Miss Copsley-Smith," I said, "may
I put one final question? What if, at the centre of your
heart, you doubt if there is a God?"

She replaced the coffee cups and sat down. "At least
you are honest," she said, "and I am so glad that you
have faced the question; no one can dodge it and stay
sane."

It was quite extraordinary to see her mannerisms,
her agitation fall from her as she spoke of God.

She said slowly, "Yes, I have been through all that,
too, and I really cannot help you; each one must settle
the problem for himself. And each one must be honest;
a half-digested argument from a text-book will carry

no conviction in the centre of the soul. There is no sensible, tangible, visible proof either way. I cannot see God with my senses but no atheist can prove that He is not there. There are rather more reasons in favour of His existence and rather more awkward questions to solve in life if He is not."

"I put it frankly to myself at the very start of my journey that I was the only being in existence whom I really knew. Rabbits, birds, other human beings, even my own parents, I see and know only in their surface life. True, I have clues to their inner lives from Christ's statement that it is from the overflow of the heart that the mouth speaks. Still, I cannot say that I know anyone except myself. Looking at myself deep down inside, at my longing to be loved, to succeed, to be safe, to be fulfilled and completed, which of the two solutions seems to fit? There isn't much choice about it, either an unexplained, ceaseless, empty craving or God Himself."

I had to answer her. "I know all that," I said, "but when I lie on the floor, I fear that I am running away from life. I am neurotic, I want love and security so I lie on the floor and create a God. If I am able to get peace from luscious green fields which have no existence, perhaps God too is a figment of my mind. Can I lie on the floor and surrender to someone who may not be there at all?"

Miss Copsley-Smith rubbed her hands together; she looked far less serious now. "That is the old argument of escapism," she cried excitedly, "and it begs the

whole question. If there is no God, then it is an escape
into fantasy to create Him; but suppose there is a God.
Why, it is just damned silly to pretend to be a man by
closing your eyes to Him. If there is a fire in a theatre
and the audience begins to move towards the exits,
do I laugh at them and shout 'Escapism'? It would
be farcical to pretend there was an exit if none existed;
it would be ridiculous not to take it if it was there.
And, in my own case, I can prove that it is there. Given
no God, my life is utterly pointless, no matter what
the philosophers in the Sunday papers say. All my
desires are blind, all my reasoning is pointless, the con-
versations which I have with myself are tommy-rot.
But I know that they are not tommy-rot. I believe in
myself sufficiently to know that, in my heart, I am
deadly sane. If you do not know this, run to a mental
home at once."

I rose to go. "Mr Dawes," she said, "you cannot
expect satisfaction in a flash. Most neurotics start with
this terrible conflict in their hearts. I suppose that you
have read Douglas Hyde's autobiography, called *I
Believed* or something like that? You will recall how
this Communist and his wife, wanting to change their
philosophy of life, read up all the proofs for the existence of God. These proofs, by the way, are far more
cogent than many pretend. When Hyde and his wife
had accepted these proofs, they did not quite know
what to do next. It was his wife who made the sanest
of suggestions that they should begin to behave as
though God really did exist. I think they both knelt

down and prayed. Prayed to an invisible God, to a
God in whom they had no faith until a few minutes
before. No doubt they, like you and me, felt pretty
foolish at first. You see nothing happens, you do not
receive at once a visible proof. Yet over the years the
reality grows, your Ego keeps on ticking, you can
enjoy a conversation in the centre of your heart. And
if you persevere in what you know to be a rational act,
adoring and loving the invisible God who made you,
it will not be so very long before you have proof indeed. Your eyes see nothing, your ears are deaf
but . . ." and here she clicked her fingers like a schoolboy . . . "there is another, alternative system of appre-
hending in the centre of your heart. You will have
proof enough that God is there."

"And are you afraid?" I asked.

"Yes," she replied, "very afraid at first and rightly;
there is no peace for human beings away from reality;
what rubbish if I was not scared stiff of God. Fear
turns to trust and trust to love when one has the
courage to lie on one's back, open the flaps and say
'Take a peep, O Lord.'"

She bustled me out. As though a dynamo had been
switched on, she suddenly came to life, tossing me
my coat, dashing to the kitchen, returning with a
gigantic loaf of French bread. "This," she said,
brandishing the roll, "is for your children and tell your
boys that I will hit them over the heads with something less yielding if they jostle me at the communion
rails again."

I stood in the street outside her flat, with the loaf as my banner and for the first time surrendered joyfully to the fear of God.

Two days later Miss Copsley-Smith was on the phone to inform us that she was sending round a Dalmatian Duck for Margery; later the same day, she rang again in a panic; Nan had got it all wrong as usual and the blue enamel bath must be returned immediately as the cousin was out of the convent and wanted it back.

3

HARRY'S RACE

RELIGION proves an absorbing subject, the most testing and the most rewarding of all the commitments made in life. Strange that it should also be presented as the most insipid, less by its enemies than by its friends. Religion probes deeper than psychology, has fashioned the course of so much history, has inspired so many of the greatest artists, writers, poets of every age. Yet the parson appears on the T.V. screen as a near moron and, sad to say, he sometimes is. Devout Christians, too, are portrayed as mean, petty, obscurantist, sometimes with only themselves to blame. In my own case, I discovered with shame at the age of thirty, that, with all its rules and regulations, my personal religion was less and less centred upon God.

Miss Copsley-Smith had certainly set me thinking and had more than supplied an alternative to those luscious green fields. I could lie on my back like the cardboard man and, with my soul wide open, accept the risk of surrendering to God. It is a risk because God is no constitutional monarch bound by democracy. If

He made me out of nothing, He can do with me exactly as He wills. Fear plays a large part in neurosis and is only controlled and mastered when one faces its extreme and most terrifying form. If there is no God, then a senseless, irrational fear lurks for ever round the corner; if there is a God, one surrenders to a master and, oddly enough, finds a lasting consolation in the fact.

The next step for me came through my boys. I have four children and Harry, the eldest, was born in 1933.

A father seems to play a secondary part in his children's training but, in secret, he stands astonished at his creative role. A learned judge once said to me after two gins and in all sincerity: "The greatest achievement of my life was to have three boys."

Both for Margery and for me the first baby was the most exciting and by far the worst. In the grand tradition of all Christian fathers, I spent many an anxious hour pacing the hospital floor. My vigil was eased from time to time by the smiling faces of Irish nurses, pretty and proud to assist at the birth of a child. At the height of suspense, I could not but smile to imagine how men would conduct themselves in such a crisis; if, say, I myself or old Ponsonby from the office were suddenly asked to bear a child.

I have a safe and honourable post. Salaries rise automatically and I should be good for an address, a dinner, a clock and a pension in a few years' time. At work each day I try, like others, to be conscientious; the truly creative part of life starts at eventide. The joy of returning home at night has not decreased with age. Perhaps there was more fun in those early years when Harry was a baby and bathing Harry was a full-time exercise.

Later there was the mad rush home to play with the children before Margery led the youngest off to bed. There was, too, the special need to consult Harry as the eldest and to give him my confidence. I loved them at the age when they were always asking questions and, also, through that tedious time when they knew all the answers; when Margery and I and our whole generation were thought to be imbecile. We had the usual games, the squabbles about baths, the normal blasphemies, all the matter-of-fact familiarity which marks a happy home. The word "familiar" offers scope for endless thought.

At one time Ludo was all the rage but as always we did things differently, Harry insisting on thirty-two counters and two Ludo boards. Each game lasted five days and produced hatred and hysteria but as soon as it was over, we had to start again. To add to the fun, we each wrote on our counters the names of enemies and friends. So Miss Copsley-Smith might be seen racing up the board in pursuit of the Canon while the Reverend Mother from Celia's convent would knock Mr Ponsonby home. It would be absurd to pretend that a middle-aged man likes playing Ludo, yet, I would not have missed a session for the world.

A farmer friend of mine, the father of five, once arrested my attention with a most surprising thought.

He said that the saddest day of his life was when John, his eldest, made his first confession, though I am sure that the little fellow had done nothing wrong in so short a span. "Oh, it's not that at all," he remarked. "The sadness comes when you cannot go into the confessional with him, when you first discover that he is a person different from yourself. John was born on the farm and in seven years he has scarcely met anyone but Peggy and myself. He looks like me, speaks like me, shares my impressions and prejudices and yet, he can walk off into the confessional to list his personal sins."

At the time I could not appreciate his grievance, later I was to share his grouse. The boys grew up looking like their mother and I liked them the better for that. Friends thought that Harry took after me but I could see no resemblance, though, every now and then, he would pull me up sharp with a mannerism which carried me back some twenty-five years. I noted with joy his immense interest in people; with shame that he had to have what he wanted at once. He knew very well and I did, too, that he could make or wreck an outing, that Margery and the smaller children were completely dependent on his moods. A father has to sit in humiliation on such painful occasions, making reparation for his own intolerance in youth.

The boys went to a public school near London; we had no option while I was overseas during the war. Both boys were above average in studies, reasonably popular, slightly condescending about games. Their reports revealed very little but the school authorities spoke kindly of them on our occasional visits during term. I missed their presence of an evening and dreaded the end of the holidays. Though they outgrew their clothes with alarming speed and looked enormous, their characters did not show any comparable change.

And then, to our surprise, Harry in his weekly letters began to mention cross-country running with increasing interest. As always with him, he wanted something, this time running shoes. As always, too, his letters were rich with apology. He would quite understand if we could not afford them, we were on no account to put ourselves out for him. Being his father, I was split in two. I would have liked to refuse for his asking was artificial and yet I wanted him to have the shoes. I had been a runner myself at school. In the next vacation Harry made some pretence of training, his conversation turned on times and records, Roger Bannister was his hero, I had to take him to the old White City for the Public School sports.

Early in the Easter term, we heard from a Mr Craig, whose boy was at the same college, that Harry was making a name for himself on the track. He himself said little at our monthly visit, tending to change the subject, belittling his own results. Margery, however, would not allow this; success in some form of athletics is always a sop to a mother's pride. Benjamin, the younger boy, was full of Harry and his skill. It seemed that Harry was a complete outsider, a fact which endeared him to the younger fry. He used to go out practising with Craig and Craig had told Johnston Major who had told Timms who had told Salmons that young Dawes was terrific and would topple many a first string from his pedestal. Harry told Benjamin to shut up, that he was talking piffle and, in frustration, took a running kick at a loose stone.

Margery was very proud, very solicitous, very ambitious and talked of Harry all the time on the journey home. She would send him Ovaltine and Bovril and would drop a line to matron about his heart. She was even prepared to start a novena to the Archangel Gabriel nine days before the all-important race was run. All the way home she chattered about his chances —Harry's, not the Archangel Gabriel's. "I don't think that you really care about the boy," she exclaimed, pouting, "you looked so bored and hardly bothered to wish him good luck."

I told her how excited and pleased I felt but explained that fathers are shy about showing feelings especially to their sons. In secret I was both proud and anxious and the race, for all its unimportance, cast a morbid shadow on the week. I found myself mooning about Harry in the office and I shared part of the tension which I knew must be his. Schoolboy contests seem so trivial to adults and I did not care whether Harry lost or won. You cannot, however, be a father and not worry about your son. Victory would mean little but I pondered the effect of success or failure on Harry's character.

In the bland, suburban world of home we could yet capture the sense of mounting tension in our letters from the boys. Harry's latest was dripping with Christian indifference, he knew that he had no chance really and was not, in fact, particularly keen to win. Benjamin was far more concerned and he, who was so careful about his money, had backed his brother up to half-a-crown. Benjamin too, let it out that old Shirty, the sports coach, was down on Harry and that all were longing to see his face when Harry won.

Margery tried every trick to persuade me to come. She said that I owed it to God and country, that I was an unnatural father, that poor Harry would be wounded for life. She wondered what the headmaster would think about our marriage if she was forced to go alone. I was informed that Mr Craig was going and had taken it for granted that I would go with him and join his party for lunch. I just could not afford to watch Harry win or lose. As good a cheat as Margery, given sufficient provocation, I built up an intricate plot with Ponsonby in the office to make sure that I would be urgently detained. I already knew that Harry would be beaten and was already suffering for him.

The great day came and Margery, at her very best and with the novena to reassure her, set off alone and cheerfully. I agreed to write Harry a note for her to give him but, as she kept peeping over my shoulder, I just scribbled "Happy Hunting" in the best public school style. Margery thought the note outrageous and said so; that I could not have shewn less unction had I been an atheist. "I do not know what has come over you," she remarked, tartly; I, of course, did.

Harry lost the race. He was not passed at the tape, he made no heroic spurt to overhaul the leaders, he never came in at all. I gathered that he started well and was still to the fore and running strongly when they left the village for the woods. He was ahead of Craig and lying third to Dawson, the eventual winner, when he lost a shoe in the mud.

Margery came home very contented to report that Harry had taken the disappointment well. She said that it was rotten bad luck, that all had agreed that it could have happened to anyone with the ground so soggy with rain. Even old Shirty had condoled with Harry in Margery's presence, telling him that he was a lazy little blighter and that if he could not bother to tie his laces properly, how could he expect to win a race. "You've got it in you," he had said in parting, "we'll see you coming in first, next year."

So that was that. Harry was not disgraced, Margery was happy, Benjamin was half-a-crown to the bad. Yet the memory of the race could not be so quickly dismissed and the thought of meeting Harry cast a shadow on the coming holidays. I puzzled in my mind the wisdom of speaking to Harry about the race. He came home in sparkling form, looking very much older and with his voice in its adolescent, husky state. His very behaviour, his thoughts, his judgments were now closely fashioned on my own. Where I could read

Margery's thoughts, there was no need to read with
Harry's, I knew instinctively what he was thinking
about. I did not have to ask the question, I knew that
the wretched race was worrying him still.

One day, quite by chance, he dropped in at the
office, partly from affection, partly because he knew
that I had come to London in the car. He wanted a
lift home. I was silent, he, bubbling with excitement,
both were attempts to evade the truth. The traffic,
happily, took all my attention but I squinted sideways
at him with pain and pride mixed in equal parts. I
knew that I must speak about the race for I was his
father, I understood the situation as not even his
mother could. For the next twenty years he might
resent it; one day he would be far happier in the knowledge that someone knew.

I did it badly and in a hurry with little tact or grace.
"By the way, Harry," I remarked. "I have been meaning to ask you for a long time, did you expect to lose
your shoe in that race?"

As I said the words, I wished that I had kept silence
for I caught in the driving-mirror a painful glimpse of
Harry's face. I knew exactly how he would answer and
was ashamed that, as his father, I had a secret peep-
hole into his heart.

"Expect to lose my shoe; how do you mean,
Dad?" he answered mildly but with tension in
his eyes.

"I only asked," I said. "Because I felt so much for
you on that occasion; I was once in a similar position

and lost my shoe on purpose; I could not win and could not face to lose."

He fought a battle with himself for one brief second; it was no surprise to me when he cut me dead for days. We drove home in complete silence and, at dinner, though he talked and laughed all round me, he had no intention of bringing me in. He was not, in any way, sulky; on what Miss Copsley-Smith would call the surface layer, he was playing a clever part. Deep inside he was wounded; it was with no malice that whenever I spoke to him, he dropped his eyes.

Yes, Harry said goodnight but without those two or three words of recognition which could have brought him peace. Who could blame him for not understanding what it means to be a father, not understanding that my knowledge of his motive implied no admonition and sprang from the very bond between us which made him everything to me.

I stayed up late that night on the excuse of writing a business letter and when Margery and the children had retired, I took a cushion from the sofa and relaxed gently on the drawing-room floor. There were now three distinct steps in this, the most therapeutic exercise in the world. I followed the Little Nun most carefully, working upwards from my toes. Banishing the luscious green fields, I copied Miss Copsley-Smith and, with all the pyschological flaps open, I whispered liturgically, "Take a peep, O Lord." But the third lesson was new to me, it had been taught to me through Harry and will last until the end of the world.

No sound is needed, just the two words "Our Father" formed in the centre of the heart. For human parenthood is but the shadow of the tolerance of a God who made me out of nothing, who knows that I lost my shoe on purpose and loves me all the more.

4

TRANSLATED FROM THE FRENCH

DESPITE the story of the Prodigal, many still fear the fatherhood of God. They will not take it literally and must always see it as but a pale reproduction of the love between a human father and his boy. It takes the humility of a Copsley-Smith to accept one's weaknesses and to believe that God loves us as we are. He could have mass produced St Teresa of Lisieux had He wished to; if He made Miss Copsley-Smith out of nothing, presumably He made her to His taste.

She once informed me that she always prayed much better in her bath. Margery was a little shocked at this and also puzzled; she was wondering how one could manage both a prayerbook and the soap. Miss Copsley Smith probably used neither, she was a genuine child in the presence of God. She took it for granted that God took some pleasure in her antics, a presumption which is certainly correct. Margery also says those tender words "Our Father" but with the reticence proper to an interview with the manager of Barclays bank.

There was time to ponder this mystery of God's intimate affection while lying on the floor. Neurotics in particular will find that the bulk of their unconscious worries stem from a wrong approach to God. Some accept no God at all and there can be no lasting answer to their fretting; they are orphans in two worlds. Others admit a God but see Him thundering on Sinai and are rightly terrified. Fear and guilt drain all the joy from many lives. The salutary fear of God is based on our nothingness and His power, not on our sinfulness and His petulant wrath. The strange fact is that even those who know this truth and love God as a father, yet retain a prim, Victorian image of what an eternal Father ought to be. Once on a pleasure boat at Anglesey with other holidaymakers, I heard on the radio news that a Sabbatarian Society had successfully stopped a Southport Flower show. Poor God!

We had a fortnight's mission in our parish not so ver' long ago. Out of loyalty to the Canon we had to endure one of the most painful exercises ever known. With due respect to the missioners, their eloquence and fervour, I came home each evening limp. Both preachers were hot on Hell and who can blame them; they had scriptural warrant for that. In fairness they might have quoted some of the more tender passages from the Gospels; I would not like my children to judge me only on my threats. Far worse, however, than these threats of punishment was their bitter, jaundiced view of life. They lambasted dancing, courting, television, drink, pools and Press. Even on the gentle sub-

ject of God's holy will they sounded dismal as though
good times come from your own contriving while God
has a vested interest in pain. The Canon himself
winced more than once for, beneath his purple
buttons, he is human and like other liturgists wants
us to lift up our hearts. To make things more farcical
still, the missioners proved to be a gay and amusing
couple when they called in private at our house. It
saddened and frightened me that two such devoted
priests should think it part of their Christian duty to
make the love of God seem so negative.

Margery also disliked this mission but, like the
ancient Jews before her, she is torn between the spirit
and the law. When I tell her that she is mentally dishonest, she assumes the manner of a Hollywood
Reverend Mother about to say "my child". Thus, she
is the one who proposes every beano and then develops scruples over the pleasure it entails. She will
suggest the movies and, as we walk there, will wonder
if we are enjoying ourselves too much. Or, she will
plan a dinner and then be afraid to offer too much
wine. Even with whiskey, she prefers four small ones
to one large one, hoping that God and her neighbours
will be more easily fooled than I.

The year that we took the caravan to Cornwall—
it was her suggestion—Margery spent a fortnight in a
flap. Was it bad for the children to be running so wild,
should she be wearing slacks as a Catholic mother,
were we spending too much money on ourselves?
Once when I shouted "Bloody hell" after nearly sever-

ing my thumb, she lectured me on my language while
plying the Elastoplast. "Was it a sin?" I asked and,
receiving no answer, I kissed her, while whispering
one of the wicked words into either ear. Margery
piously hoped that God would forgive me and,
to show herself both forgiving and broadminded, proposed a visit to a neighbouring inn. On the way back
she stopped to announce that we were roués, ready
to let our little family perish in a quicksand provided
we could have our drink. That night she took double
the time over her evening prayers. In answer to my
comment, she said that it was examining my conscience for me that had held her up.

It was then that we met the French Abbé who was
to change all our attitudes to sin. .

We had motored that morning from Padstow and
parked after midday in open country between Hayle
and Portreath. There were far fewer caravans then
than now. Margery was unpacking on a grassy bank
within a hundred yards of the sand. Up ran Benjamin
to announce that it was a rotten place, that we must
move at once, that a party of revolting people were
camping round the corner from our site. Like all
middle-class English children, he resented such intru-
sion and only wanted the entire Cornish coast-line to
himself.

Harry, next, sauntered up in the style of a school
prefect to inform us that the revolting people were
French. The words were just out of his mouth when
a group of some ten young men and boys came into

sight. They looked slightly French with their be-
draggled uniforms and berets and some of them
seemed to be wearing their small brother's pants. They
were laughing, smiling, pushing, singing, with two
of the younger ones running ahead.

I was surprised to note, as they came nearer, one
most unusual looking man. He was dressed in black
in a suit two sizes too big. The ends of his trousers
were stuffed into thick, white bedsocks which, in turn,
had been squeezed into thin, black, pointed boots. He
wore a beret but no collar and looked like a runaway
monk. A home-rolled cigarette, yellow and crooked,
dangled from his lips. It was jerking up and down as
he played an imaginary trumpet, making bugle noises
through his lips.

Harry, Benjamin and the girls stood in a defiant
square, staring like the guards at Waterloo. Ashamed
at their appalling shyness, I overdid the greeting, wav-
ing with a dirty dish cloth in my hand. The small,
runaway monk stopped trumpeting to smile. Next, he
bounded across the belt of seaweed and, with his boys
giggling in the background, solemnly shook hands.
When he came to Celia, he tickled her chin, and, un-
expectedly, she returned his smile.

In excellent, studied English he announced himself
as the Abbé Delpierre. When we said that we were
Roman Catholics, he looked a little disappointed as
though Protestants would have proved a pleasant
change on holiday. He explained that he had taught
English in Cairo, had served in the Middle East with

British forces and so spoke our language reasonably well. "It is because of this," he said, "that I must bring these pupils to England for the summer to practise your excellent tongue. You forgive my speech, I am a little rusty and"—placing his hand across his collar —"you forgive me also my dress."

Margery in her best convent French asked if we could do anything to help him but he at once checked her. "You must always speak in English, we practise for five hours every day." He again shook hands all round, jumped sideways across the seaweed, waved with his companions and marched happily away.

Once the French boys had gone, our children were very sorry; Celia in particular wanted the little priest to come again. Her prayers were answered when two French lads appeared. They wanted us to lend them the English morning paper for their exercise. "Father," they said, very slowly and shyly, "would be very content if you would please correct our English," but before we could do anything about it they had turned tail and fled.

Ten minutes later two of the younger boys arrived, nice lads with mobile, intelligent faces, to offer us a rather battered copy of *Figaro*. They, too, drew a deep breath to announce that Father would be very content if we would, please, correct their English but again without offering us much chance. Margery detained them long enough to ask if they were enjoying England and what they admired most. They replied rapidly and by heart that they liked best the whiskey, the Guards, bowler hats, policemen and the monarchy. They scampered off with a tin of toffees which Margery solemnly presented; Harry added grandly that we were pushing the Entente Cordiale just a little too far.

Then came the Abbé Delpierre himself and Margery from nowhere produced a bottle of wine. He preferred beer. Refusing a glass, he drank from the bottle, standing and then said, laughingly, that English beer went down too quickly and that he would like to change his mind and have some wine. For the wine, he sat on the grass by our side.

He was an astonishing little man, alert, sensitive, kindly but, like so many Frenchmen, unemotional and as hard as nails. He could smile sweetly but his critical, inquisitive eyes were never still. All his gestures were expressive, hands, shoulders, fingers, eyes, eyebrows coming into play. If these proved insufficient, he would shoot a leg forward to kick the sand. Bien, Tiens and Chien, suitably interjected, changed the mood of the discussion in a flash. He would lie back with his head on the sand to let the smoke from his cigarette curl upwards but I noticed that he did not maintain this relaxed position for long. His face was lined with fatigue but, as with so many Frenchmen, he found more rest in developing a theme.

I cannot hope to reproduce his exact expressions, the sudden pauses, the impatient little gestures when he could not find the exact English word. He spoke English astonishingly well. From time to time he would rub the palms of his hands together with extra-ordinary vigour and this diversion normally expressed delight. When he used a French word, he would not go on until he had given a translation, so anxious was he to improve his English and to speak it well. When Margery asked him about his boys, he dismissed them with an irritable flick of the fingers. "With any luck," he said, "they will all drown themselves."

For a while we spoke about ourselves. He told us about his mother, his Citroën, parked in Calais, the Common Market and the songs of Père Aimé Duval. He, the Abbé, came from a farm in the Vosges, was now part-time chaplain to the Young Christian Workers, had served in Syria with the French Army and had been associated with the resistance movements after his repatriation in 1941. Politely he inquired after Sir Winston Churchill and the Queen.

"And now what?" he asked, rolling himself a cigarette.

I said that we had been talking about God.

"A very good subject," he remarked, wagging his head. "But, perhaps, a little too big."

I told him of my lying on the floor and about the Little Nun's advice. Margery, switching on her St Elizabeth of Hungary expression, added rather meanly that she found herself married to a religious maniac.

"That," said the Abbé, "is a sound premise to start from, but one would not normally associate religious mania with the British Isles. Judging by the British officers I knew in Cairo, I formed the impression that God was rather like the headmaster of one of your public schools; you could count on him to behave like an Englishman in a crisis and for the rest, well, he was harmless if not disturbed."

Next, we spoke a little about nerves. He agreed that tension was a problem even in his own country and that people talked about neurosis too easily. "It is our generation which has given a label to a state of uncertainty and hesitation which all other ages took in their stride."

I pressed him further on this.

"Neurosis," he said, "is always the beginning, never the end." Do you ever read the French journal *Cahiers Mystiques de Limoges?* No! So much the better, I am now able to borrow the thoughts of the learned author and pass them on to you as my own."

He paused and moved his head sideways, like a woman arranging flowers in a vase. "A great many saints," he said, "showed, what we would call, neurotic symptoms at the start of their quest for God. St Teresa of Avila suffered many pains, disturbances and imaginings when she started praying during the time which she called her 'double' life. St Teresa of Lisieux was not much better, full of self-pity and easily reduced to tears. Her piety was worried and artificial for some years. St Francis de Sales had, what we would call today, a nervous breakdown while he was an undergraduate at Padua. His was a very worrying problem; he thought after reading Calvinist doctrines that he was damned. St Margaret Mary was very neurotic in her convent; her trouble was that she could not swallow cheese. Even St Ignatius of Loyola, a middle-aged soldier, passed through a worrying time after his conversion; he saw a hole in the cloister of the Dominican convent in which he was staying and was tempted to jump in and kill himself. St John of God actually pretended to be mad and was locked up in an asylum —a most curious symptom this. Two prelates wanted to put Don Bosco away in an institution; he must have given some grounds for such a step. There are many more examples but, Madame ..." and he turned to bow towards Margery ... "one day your husband will be the Blessed Henry Dawes, patron of Neurotics and then they will write many big books about him, recording all the crosses heaped on him by his heartless wife."

Margery changed her saintly smile to her Salome smirk.

"Neurosis is only the beginning?" I asked.

"Yes, if you recognise it for what it is and master it. It is what one might call suppressed ambition, a state of worry because we are so anxious to succeed. Did you read last April's issue of *Lettres Psychologiques et Mystiques de Lyon*? No! Good, I am able to continue as a learned man."

It was a glorious afternoon with the sun playing on the water; the deep, luminous blue of the Cornish coast was ravishing to the eye. The Abbé sipped his wine. "Almost all the great psychologists would agree," he said, "that neurosis is a certain symptom of self-centredness. The more neurotic, the more self-centred though, perhaps, I should put it the other way round." He turned the phrases round with his hands. "The more self-centred, the more neurotic because the will for power is so very great. Ambition to succeed, deep down in your heart, will produce neurosis when it is blocked by outside impediments. Some people are so ambitious that they work their minds and bodies too hard. Others feel that they are not going to succeed because health, environment, money, social prejudice is against them and then, unconsciously, they must look around and find an excuse. They know their own excellence and they lack the humility just to sit down and admit failure. So much do they esteem the opinion of others that they must be able to explain their failure to their friends. 'I, too, would have done as well,' they like to say, 'only I had poor health, a cruel father, class prejudice against me or—and this is far more dangerous—I was so holy that I did not want to succeed in this world.'"

He bowed to me, "So, Blessed Henry Dawes, it is easy to be neurotic, it is very much harder to become a saint. You may lie on the floor comme-ça—you may say the Pater Noster comme-ça—you may even induce the stigmata by auto-suggestion but you cannot so easily become a little child comme-ça," and with an easy gesture he pointed gracefully to Celia and her little sister, shrieking with excitement by the waves.

He filled up his glass, sipped it, balanced it on the

sand beside him while he fell to rubbing the palms of his hands. "It is easy," he said, "to feel holy on such a day and given a bottle of wine."

"Have you read," he asked, turning to me, "have you read the current issue of *La Revue Ascétique de Chartres*? No! The author there makes the point that all words prefixed by the conjunction *dis-*, meaning *two-*, *apart-*, *separate*, are almost always unhappy words. I do not know if I am familiar enough with your language but I can think of disappointment, disillusion, disagreeable, dissatisfaction and, perhaps, distress. There may be many more. All these words suggest duplicity and duplicity means conflict, indecision, unhappiness. There is always unhappiness where men and women lead double lives. Our Lord Jesus Christ said that we cannot serve two masters at once, yet so many attempt it and neurosis in one form or another is the result. The centre of our hearts is double and the conflict is painful indeed. In almost every language we have mirrored this duplicity as when we say 'double talk', 'second thoughts', 'double-faced'."

"And this," I asked. "This is the root of sin?"

"Precisely," he returned, nodding in agreement. "Sin is always a self-centred choice for my own immediate gain. I find that there is very much humbug in speaking about sin. We like to make lists and to say that this is a big sin and that is a little sin but we forget the essential that nothing is a sin unless it is due to this self-centredness."

He leant back, plainly annoyed with most Christians and especially with himself. He made those funny hissing noises, heard in Paris during a heated argument. He was smoking furiously. I could sense his genuine anger against such bourgeois pettiness. This trait, so common in Frenchmen, is one that one must admire very much.

So we paused for some time, drinking and smoking and, when he resumed, he had changed his manner and was most precise. "Why," he asked, "do we look further than the Passion of Christ for a picture of ourselves? Here the story of our daily life is admirably described. We see no impatience, no impure thoughts, no using of swear words but that self-centredness which led to so terrible an end. I note that all those who played a key part in the crucifixion were, on the surface, good men. Pilate had a sense of justice, Peter was devoted, Judas had enough virtue to be picked out of hundreds to be one of the twelve. Even the Pharisees were churchgoers on a big scale. Next, they all loved and admired Christ, they knew that His cause was a noble one and they admitted that He was innocent. But they were double through self-centredness. They wanted two things at once; they wanted Christ to be successful but, in their hearts, they wanted their own interests more. Pilate wanted his job, Peter wanted his skin, Judas wanted his money, Herod wanted to show off before his friends. Even the Pharisees only wanted to remain top men. None of them would have minded going to confession to accuse themselves of a little impatience, 'a little greedy, my mind wandered during my prayers'. What they should have said was 'Dear Lord, I am very devoted to you but I love myself far more.'

"They could not say that except poor Peter when he wept. Judas threw the money back, Pilate washed his hands in public, Herod made friends with Pilate, the Pharisees scrupled to enter the Governor's house on the feast day but they could not face their real guilt. They reproduced the sin of Adam and Eve and all that nonsense of hiding in the bushes and blaming each other for their fault. I have often wondered what would have happened to our world if Adam and Eve had behaved as little children, rushed out naked from the bushes to admit how self-centred they were. They were afraid of God; Judas killed himself from fear, the Pharisees were afraid and put a guard by the tomb, Pilate's wife had nightmares, why? because they were all double, they served two masters, they could not admit their self-centredness even to themselves. True contrition wipes away all fear."

He paused to consult his watch. "I must be going," he said. "I have ruined all your relaxation and I have happily almost forgotten my boys. I do not know if I have even answered your original question but I feel very strongly on this question of self-centredness. I feel that the symptoms of this cancer, sulking, deceit, flattery, jealousy, spite, which were all present in the Passion, do not worry us enough. That is why we are afraid of God. I have seen the same thing happen with my own two eyes. Let me tell you a story in which I myself was involved.

"You know of the French resistance movement in the last war? Yes. It sprang from defeat and shame and was motivated by a burning love for France. We Frenchmen recognise still that it started with the bravery of many of your people who came to share the risks with us. Many, many a time I sat in the fields at night watching for British planes to fly over, waiting for British agents to land. It was always an inspiration to greet them in the darkness and to shake their hands.

"We were not idle either and many, quite ordinary Frenchmen risked their lives. When the resistance group was forming in my region, my brother was one of the very first to volunteer. I, as a priest, could not take part—they called me jokingly the chaplain—my main duties were to console the dying and, at night, to bury the dead.

"I never knew a group of men more loyal or more lovable, Charles, Henri, Jean, the brothers Duval, Lepoutre, Mardyke, etc., etc., I still see them before me now. They were both brave and competent but they would have achieved next to nothing without the inspiration of Raoul. He was the one chosen as chief by the first, famous British agent and we respected this choice.

"Raoul was more than the head of our group, he was the heart as well. An extraordinary man, smiling, debonair, quick to improvise, slow to panic, ready to presume the best from everyone. He raised ordinary men and women far higher than they would have risked. Nor did he hate the Germans as so many others did, he just loved liberty and France.

"You know the kind of work that they undertook, the clandestine meetings, the secret radio, the night vigils in the hedges, the flares and lights in the right pattern to guide the British planes. These Frenchmen were at their ordinary work all day and then stayed up all night, risking their lives to smuggle British soldiers and agents towards the frontier, to store arms and ammunition against the day of liberty. Raoul was present at every attempt, he hatched the plans with his uncanny gift of anticipation and somehow generated the extra courage needed when the crisis came. I would reckon that, in the darkest moment in our history, there was no resistance group as competent, as courageous and as determined as our own. Raoul may well have been one of the most outstanding leaders ever produced by France."

The Abbé was speaking quietly now, almost in a whisper, but his eyes were angry and I caught in his voice a rasping note of pain.

"At the darkest moment," he repeated, "when Hitler seemed so secure and the task of fighting for freedom looked so futile, our group produced a standard of courage which has never been surpassed. I knew them all so well. And yet it was I who first saw the change in their attitude, so unexpected, at the very moment when the Nazi Empire began to crack. When there was no hope in this world they were brimful of courage, but as the day of liberation came gradually nearer, this courage seemed to ebb away with success. Though they attempted bigger and better raids and showed a bravado which astonished Europe, I, the chaplain, could note a painful change.

"Oh yes, they were still devoted, still followed Raoul with exact obedience and implicit love. But a nagging, querulous note crept into their discussions. 'What about my poor old Father?' 'The Nazis are not such a bad crowd really.' 'Liberation will come anyway without our efforts.' 'Watch out, we do not want another gang to seize power when we have won the fight.' I once heard one of them say, 'Why should we risk our necks for the Americans and the British; they did little for us when we were down?' So some seemed to be holding back a little, some joined the Communist guerrillas, one or two tried to help influential friends in the neighbouring towns. One even suspected that someone inside the group was passing information to the Germans; on two occasions our most secret plans were anticipated and we saw one of our bravest, the radio expert, dragged away to death.

"Raoul would not allow a word of doubt to be spoken in his presence about his beloved group. I tried to warn him but he brushed me aside. All that he would ask was : 'Am I too imperious? Am I intolerant? You must tell me, Father, if I have changed. The strain is greater now and we are all exhausted; we must expect a little friction but the fight is nearly over and we must not fail.'

"I could see a change in Raoul. He was looking older, his hair was quite grey, his eyelids were twitching but he kept his laughter and could still cheer and brace the whole group. I felt, however, that he alone remained entirely devoted, not thinking of future peace and power, not seeking to make friends in high places, not looking for safety and promotion, still ready to die for France. His only question about the group was typical: 'Am I changing, they seem a little afraid of me?' He noticed this fear, he noted that some of them did not tell him of their troubles, rarely spoke to him privately. Typical of him, he thought that the change was in himself.

"When I warned him not to be too trusting, he would look at me with horror and dismay. 'Father,' he would say, 'You know Henri, Charles, Jean and the others; we love each other, not one of them will ever betray the group. I would stake my life on that.' Oddly enough I could not believe that any one of them would prove a traitor and yet I was well aware of secret duplicity. 'Raoul,' I said, 'they are afraid of you because they are double, the two go together, it is an unfailing sign.'

"Of course I was right. Any fool could have told a mile away that men, who are thinking of their own position, will let you down when it pays. As soon as there was hope of security, promotion, ambition in this world, selfless heroism died.

"Our last great expedition took place just after your D-Day; instructions came from London to blow up a

railway embankment to stop the movement of a pan-
zer division towards Normandy. One might say that
this was the great opportunity for which we had been
fighting and preparing through three, long, painful
years.

"Raoul produced his plans as usual, simple,
courageous and direct. I was present at the final brief-
ing in the cellar under Raoul's mill. For once he did
not really need to commit the whole group to action
and he asked for volunteers. Everyone volunteered,
everyone felt that this might be the final sortie and all
wanted to be present at the end. Raoul gave way, reassured, and I myself was deeply moved by this show
of spirit and even regretted my previous anxiety. He
changed his plans to fit the increased numbers and
issued clear orders to each pair. All were in high spirits
but two look-outs were posted and I recall two
revolvers on the table in case the Germans staged a
sudden raid.

"We had supper together, Raoul sitting at the head.
After the meal we all raised our glasses to each other
and then someone proposed a toast of Raoul. Frenchmen are normally a little cynical but, on this one
occasion, everyone sprang to his feet. As always before
an outing like this, Raoul invited me to say a prayer
before they went. Not all Frenchmen are practising
Christians but in our part of France the number of
believers is high. All through those dangerous years,
a prayer for safety had been offered and on this, as

on other occasions, quite a few would come to me for absolution before risking death.

"Well, they all slipped away in pairs and there was a long silence followed by the distant sound of an explosion and some rifle shots. I paced up and down the cellar alone for nearly two hours, praying and sweating, waiting for the freedom fighters to return. They came in ones and twos and their stories differed, some thought that the raid had been successful, others found the German sentries alerted and were driven off. No one seemed to think that anyone had been hurt. No, they had not seen Raoul or any of the others, each pair had its own detailed task to do. Three charges of dynamite had been planned but at least one of the pairs assigned to place it had been unable to reach the line.

"We waited and each new arrival sought to encourage the others: 'He'll be back,' they said one to another, 'it is still early; he had the furthest to go.'

"He never returned. He alone died on that final raid, the climax of three years of heroic work.

"It was like Calvary," said the little French Abbé, jumping up in agitation and gazing for a moment out to sea. "Calvary, yes, but with two slight differences for Christ died in shame while Raoul was accorded a hero's funeral as soon as the liberation was achieved. They took up his body from the place where I had laid it beneath the trees. Covered with the tricolour he was paraded round the streets. I did not attend this final salute—I had not the heart to do so—but I am told that all of the others were there.

"And the other difference—well, Christ was pierced by a lance through the heart; Raoul was killed with bullets—not German bullets—when I buried him I saw that he had been shot from behind."

"Yes," he said slowly, as he walked with me towards the seaweed. "They all loved him but they double-crossed him in the end. That was why they were afraid of him."

"And your brother's name?" I asked.

"Raoul," he said.

5

CANONS TO RIGHT OF THEM

THE Canon is the least neurotic person known to me. He moves slowly, smiles evenly, chuckles softly, speaks wisely with a strict economy of words. Without any lack of sympathy, he yet remains aloof and undisturbed. He will return without a tremor from a heart-breaking sick call to resume *The Times* crossword where he had left it off. His sermons are shrewd but uninspiring; you fall asleep with an easy conscience and wake loving God the more. A kindly soul, the Canon nurses a quiet grudge against French Reverend Mothers, priests wearing berets and against those thin, tapering candles so popular in France.

The Canon has known us for many years, for so many years that he may call me "the mystic" without offending and may flirt with Margery in a mild, ecclesiastical way. When I told him about the Abbé Delpierre, he made no comment but I noticed that his pipe began to twitch. Here was a portent which we, his parishioners, note with awe. The last time it twitched, those who had been pressing for a return to the old Westminster Hymnal abandoned that beloved book for good.

The Canon nurses a strange suspicion against all continental clerics but this does not seem to spoil his holidays abroad. True, he normally travels with an English auxiliary bishop and the two will sit in some suitable grove—say the Borghese gardens—to pore over yesterday's *Daily Telegraph* and last week's cricket scores. The Canon is a devoted alumnus of one of those English seminaries long settled on the Continent. He is convinced that English ecclesiastical practice, rightly applied, would prove a shot in the arm for the Universal Church. A simple man, he fosters a burning love for Saints Bede, Dunstan, Elphege or for any other holy persons, male or female, who were lucky enough to practise sanctity in the British Isles. As proof of his tenets, Kipling reposes next to Fortescue and Manning on his shelves.

The Canon does not really approve of my praying on the floor. When first I heard him say to Margery, "Well and how is the mystic?" I was secretly worried and my mind flew back to the unhappy Mr Owles. Now I know, or hope that I know, that he is only leg-pulling; he will often tease me and Margery quotes his verdict when her own case is exceptionally weak.

When the Canon frisks me about prayer, I tell him that his liturgical practice is snobbish, suitable only for High Church converts and for the Cherubim and Seraphim. He agrees reluctantly that liberty in prayer is essential though he thinks that some of the saints went a little too far in this respect. "Mostly the Latin saints," he will say with a chuckle. "You don't find Bede and Becket lying on the floor, deluding themselves." He once admitted to me that he was not enthusiastic about hermits, virgins or mystics, that he liked his saints to be British diocesan bishops and/or Doctors of the Church.

The Canon's scruple lies in this, that mystics and other unusual people so easily fool themselves. He would not deny that God may reveal Himself to a soul if He wants but he doubts if God often does. He sees all unusual forms of prayer as a kind of presumption. "If I ever have any lights in prayer," he said once, "I take it for granted that these must come from the devil; I am far too wicked a man for God to be favouring me in this way."

I found this attitude disturbing and on many occasions we joined in a theological dispute. It says much for the Canon that he allows a layman to air an opinion and does not treat us all as secondary modern types.

I told him that limiting prayer to a mumbled Latin formula sucked all the joy from prayer and drove thousands from the Church. He told me that lying on the floor and breathing deeply merely increased the carbon dioxide in the blood stream and produced a state of coma, quite independent of God. I told him that I had many saints on my side, he told me that I also had thousands of Eastern mystics who used exactly the same methods to get in touch with their pagan gods.

We, then, both laughed and told each other that we were saying the same thing really and that it was silly to get hot and bothered, arguing about prayer. After that we fell on each other hammer and tongs. Margery rarely intervenes in these disputations, she contents herself with whistling "Faith of Our Fathers" in the wings.

The Canon enjoys an argument and one may gauge the fortunes of the battle by the way in which he treats his pipe. Should he advance, he pokes the stem at his opponent as though to force home his point. On the other hand, in moments of crisis, he sucks it and on some very critical occasions looks as though he might swallow it whole. If he pauses to fill or to light it, he never lowers his eyes for a moment but glares balefully at you over the bowl. I have known him to address himself to his pipe in the heat of the moment and to bang it down on the table as a final gesture of reproach.

He had to concede on one occasion that he himself has never suffered from nerves. Once or twice he has been in a slight panic when intoning a preface without glasses or putting a mitre on a bishop who kept on moving his head. Again, the Canon admits that he dislikes all psychology except that taught by St Thomas Aquinas in the medieval schools. He and I love each other but the unity of faith does not prevent us in disagreeing on everything save the Apostles' Creed.

When we turn to the Bible, I love the Canticle of

Canticles which he thinks rather naughty, he loves the measurements of the Temple and the rubrical details of Deuteronomy. I am for mystical spouses, he, for whole burned offerings; I like virgins and martyrs, he confessors and bishops, I, *the Cloud of Unknowing*, he, the *Liber Usualis*, I, Gerard Manley Hopkins, he Cardinal Manning and Melchisedech. After every dispute, he would hold up his pipe as a pledge of peace between us and we would both admit with admiration the many facets of the One and Undivided God.

Yet, in the course of our many disputes which lasted for hours and seemed to lead nowhere, the Canon, in bits and pieces, built up a very impressive lesson for us all. We neurotics especially will greatly profit from his wisdom, so very British and so sound a safeguard in the delicate matter of progress in prayer. For there is no greater danger than self-deception and this is particularly true in the type of relaxed prayer which I have tried to describe. Mind you, I would not now abandon it for the Canon or for anyone else. This sudden intimacy with God, the consciousness of His presence, the ability to pray without words and to free oneself from imagination offers a new dimension and makes prayer an integral part of daily life. Yet the Canon is right when he refuses to accept peace, release from worry, increase in confidence as necessary signs that prayer is pleasing to God. The proof of progress does not lie in feelings and may best be judged on one very concrete point.

While I had been pondering The Canticle of Canticles, the Canon with typical British phlegm had been working his way through the Bible collecting historical clues in his search for God. In consequence of this search, he had come to the practical and painful conclusion, missed by most romantic people, that it is far easier "to love the Lord thy God with thy whole heart and soul and mind and strength" than it ever will be "to love thy neighbour as thyself". "You may lie on the floor if you like," he said, pointing the stem of his pipe in my direction, "but only if it is helping you to become more charitable. There is no other test." I had to admit this point and when I told him that St Teresa of Avila agreed with his diagnosis, he blushed like a seminarian.

It was touching to learn how this old man had taken the Bible and worked slowly through it for detailed information about the most deadly of all sins. He had been forced to the opinion that of all the wickedness known to man and revealed by God for our warning, jealousy holds pride of place. As he puffed his pipe he proved it, starting with the first murder when Cain murdered his brother Abel out of jealousy. He could not stomach that his brother's sacrifice should seem more pleasing to God. Joseph was sold into slavery by his brothers and sisters because he had dreamed that one day he would be more important and powerful than they. So they plotted murder, then sold him as a slave, then acted a lie in dipping his coat in blood and informing his parents that he had been devoured by animals. They stood and watched the agony of their old father Jacob because they could not tolerate their younger brother faring better than themselves. The Canon thrives on facts.

He spent ten minutes on the book of Kings, on the terrible story of Saul and David; Saul, a king, chosen by God as the first King of the Jewish people and yet jealous of a lad. Four times this middle-aged man tried to destroy the boy David out of jealousy. Four times he tried, four times he failed, four times he apologised and begged forgiveness, four times he started to plot again. He ended with his kingdom shattered and his reign in ruins because he hated to have a boy more popular than himself.

The smoke of the Canon's pipe curled upwards like the smoke of sacrifice. "David," he said, "was a king, certainly a mystic and the backbone of the liturgy, yet he managed, between psalms, to murder one of his soldiers because he envied him his wife. David's sin is the more frightening because he did not seem to know that he had done it and it took a full-time prophet to stand before him and to open his eyes to the fact. He, the King, with a whole nation of girls to choose from, wanted this soldier's wife. He had him killed, and killed in battle fighting for David, and had the nerve to proclaim a day of national mourning for the fallen hero whom he had deliberately placed in the most dangerous part of the line." The Canon poked the stem of his pipe in the general direction of David, then banged it on the table in a graphic gesture of disgust.

In his own British way the Canon was making the same point as the Abbé Delpierre. So, finally to Calvary itself and he stood up with his pipe-stem pointing to the heavens to apostrophise the Jewish priests. "Law abiding citizens," he said, "scrupulous in fasting, punctilious rubricians and yet your epitaph, the most terrible ever written, is read in St John's gospel. 'It was because of envy that they did these things.'" He sat down abruptly and remarked almost in a whisper, "priests who could not allow the Son of God to be more successful than themselves."

As though almost ashamed of his show of feelings, the Canon sat puffing his pipe in silence for some time. He is normally a man of few words, especially about himself. On this occasion, though he did not speak, he was fighting a battle and one could sense that he was considerably distressed. When finally he spoke, he seemed to be talking to himself. "It did not end on Calvary," he said. "It was the main fault of the twelve apostles and Christ Himself rebuked them twice, once at the Last Supper, for arguing about who was the greatest, for fighting for the top place. Paul met it at Corinth where the Church was divided between Paul, Apollo and Cephas. We saw it in the English Church at the time of Becket, at the reformation, even between Manning and Newman, two Cardinals. In all my long life as a priest, this has been the sin which has caused the greatest trouble, between brothers and

sisters, parents and children, matrons and nurses, secu-
lar priests and religious, in parishes, hospitals, football
teams, seminaries and schools. Some of the greatest
work ever undertaken has been smashed by this, the
good man's sin. You can understand how worried one
must be about prayer, mysticism, visions unless one is
on one's guard about jealousy. Graces and lights in
prayer are not from God unless they lead us to control ourselves in this respect. That, at least, is how I
see it; I must leave it to you and to the mystics to get
round the Bible's solid facts."

Again the old man fell into a strained silence and
pulled viciously at his pipe. Twice he sat forward as
though to speak and twice leaned back. Then, of a
sudden, he raised his eyes in my direction and, un-
expectedly, smiled.

"Years ago," he said, "and in another place so you
will not know it, I myself saw the ravages of jealousy.
It is a trashy little story, scarcely worth the telling,
save that it shows how harm is done almost unconsciously.

"Here was a large Victorian parish not far from
London with a crowded population and a Pugin style
church. All over Britain the towns had started spread-
ing and the jerry builders were experimenting with
their first hideous housing estates. The parish priest,
an able and far-sighted man, was quick to assess his
future needs. He acquired a site in an outlying part
of the parish and on it a ramshackle stone building,
once a Salvation Army citadel and then a laundry and

now falling into decay. The architects agreed that it could be sufficiently restored for present requirements and it was planned to open it as a chapel of ease.

"Transport was not so easy in those days so one of the younger curates was sent to the new mission and to live in digs. He returned to the parish church once a week for dinner, bath and confession, otherwise he was on his own. Here was a lonely, testing job for there was little money or co-operation and the problems in a new area are very great. Of these the human element is by far the worst.

"The parish priest enjoyed a high reputation in the diocese as a man of piety and parts. He consulted the young curate and encouraged him, did all in his power to make the assignment easy, warned him of the likely dangers, especially of parochial jealousy. The two priests even made a private novena together and when a parish priest makes a novena there is joy before the angels of God.

"The chapel of ease was initiated with a grand bazaar and social in the local pub. The parish priest came himself to introduce the curate and to beg the parishioners for support. He pointed out that many would probably prefer the older church, many would find the little chapel cramped and dingy but he asked them all to sink their differences that the Kingdom of God might spread. He held out hopes that in the not too distant future, a new independent parish would be formed. After the parish priest came the curate begging for assistance and promising the earth. Then the

Byrnes, the MacIntyres, the Stephensons and the Belgian Countess rose to pledge unqualified help.

"The initial troubles were very great as had been expected but these did not turn on lack of funds. The congregation was generous indeed and the Belgian Countess produced the most wonderful material for furnishings. As I have already hinted, jealousy proved the biggest headache in a task like this.

"The Byrnes were brothers, both with large families, both Irish dockers from Cork. Between them they could almost have filled the little church. Unfortunately Tom Byrne had a grievance against his brother and thought that the curate consulted Mike too much. He therefore would not come to the new chapel if his brother's family was there.

"The MacIntyres lived in a small house by the gas works, Jim was manager and his two sisters kept house for him. All were devout and with so large a statue of Our Lady of Lourdes on the sideboard that one felt the urge to take one's cup of tea on one's knees. They almost made the tea with Lourdes water, at least on big feasts. This did not prevent them from refusing to mix with the Byrnes and of nursing a slight grudge against the Stephensons.

"Mr Stephenson was the town surveyor and the MacIntyres thought that his family gave themselves airs. As Mrs Stephenson, the surveyor's mother, manned the chapel harmonium, the MacIntyres were tempted to stay away. In fact they developed an out-size devotion to Our Lady of Perpetual Succour and went to the Redemptorist Monastery for Mass on Sundays to pray at her shrine.

"The young curate was very grieved about all this for he was full of fervour and could not understand how Christians could be so petty in the cause of Our Lord. He often spoke to the parish priest about it but this older and wiser man told him not to worry, that Christ suffered the same annoyance and that this was a trial which all priests must expect to bear. The parish priest advised him to put his trust in the Belgian Countess, a remarkable woman who would certainly be above such trivial jealousy. He said that he would himself ask her to befriend and advise the younger priest.

"She certainly was a remarkable woman, a widow who gave all her time and money to the Church. She worked daily on the new vestments, she advised the curate on so many of his problems, she even achieved wonders in bringing the Byrnes and MacIntyres to speak to each other and to the Stephensons. Tom Byrne went so far as to attend the new chapel on Sundays provided that his brother and his family knelt on the other side of the aisle. The MacIntyres said 'Good morning' to Mrs Stephenson on very special feasts. The parish priest was delighted with all this and congratulated his curate, informing him that the Belgian Countess had spoken with unlimited enthusiasm about his zeal.

"So the mission grew but how rarely is there a happy ending in everyday parish life. A certain friction developed between the new mission and the old established church. As the mission grew and the loyalty of the people was more effective, certain awkward situations arose. The first rift was over the bazaar which the parish priest decided should be a joint affair with profits proportionately shared. The curate would have given way on this but the Belgian Countess advised him not to, she thought that it was necessary for the new mission to stand on its own two feet. A great friend to the parish priest, she went to see him and he, a holy and reasonable man, at once gave way. He spoke to the curate after Sunday dinner and told him that such silly little differences must not be allowed to occur again. He said that parish rivalries were poisonous and out of place. He did however ask that the curate himself should speak to him about such subjects and not allow the Belgian Countess to come in his place. 'She is a wonderful person,' he said, 'but like all women she is a little interfering and one cannot be too careful as a priest.'

"Came Christmas and the parishioners on the housing estate took it for granted that they would be having a Midnight Mass of their own. The curate announced it and the Belgian Countess started preparing a new antependium in Cloth of Gold. Back in the presbytery, the parish priest and the other curates heard about it and pulled his leg unmercifully about the new frontal and his contacts with the continental aristocracy. They thought that he was moving towards a High Church position and would soon be introducing the vernacular. I think he took it in good part. Plans for Midnight Mass were developing and a list in the porch invited each family to buy one figure for the Christmas crib. The curate himself was good with his hands and he made the stable and manger and was even planning a waterfall. A choir was formed for the Christmas carols and even Tom Byrne, who had never been heard to sing a note since he came from Ireland, decided to try his luck on 'Silent Night'.

"At the very last moment the parish priest vetoed the Midnight Mass. His arguments were sensible, that he had not been consulted, that the bishop would not like it, that it was right on this one great family feast that all parishioners should come to their parish church. He also said at dinner to the other curates that perhaps Fr X was a little imprudent and taking on too much. Fr X, when he heard, pleaded in vain, apologised most humbly, pointed out how great would be the disappointment if the ban was maintained.

"The curate and the Belgian Countess went into a huddle, trying to decide what next to do. The Countess was a brave woman and, eventually, without a word to the curate, she went down again to see the parish priest. She won her case. The parish priest was charming and told the curate of his change of mind. That Midnight Mass was celebrated with considerable splendour and the church, of course, was packed. One or two people even came to the chapel of ease from the parish church. The Byrnes, the MacIntyres, the Stephensons along with the Countess and the curate almost raised the roof. At Christmas dinner, parish priest and curates teased Fr X about his sensational achievement, his golden antependium, his crib with a living fountain, his choir, and, presumably, his swollen collection plate.

"About two weeks after Christmas the curate received notice of a move. The parish priest informed him that the bishop needed him for another post. Curates are frequently shifted and expect as much. There was a very real sense of sorrow in the housing estate. The Belgian Countess gave an informal dinner and all the Byrnes, the MacIntyres, the Stephensons were there. The Countess fashioned the butter to the shape of a biretta and there were many touching presents round the curate's plate. The parish priest himself in a cordial speech of thanks praised the efforts of his curate and was glad to think that the diocese would gain by their sad loss.

"The curate was, for a moment, overwhelmed. It broke his heart to leave this, his first mission, in which he had done so well. He spoke to his fellow curates about his suspicions but they told him not to be a fool. The parish priest gave him a paternal talk before he left, begging him not to take such moves too seriously. A bishop has many problems and priests of all people should be ready to take up such crosses as though they were given by Christ Himself.

"The curate left," said the Canon, "and, in his new parish, worked reasonably well. The first fervour was a little tarnished and for many years he nursed a grievance that he had been moved out of jealousy. The very vice which he had worked to stamp out in the Byrnes, the MacIntyres and the Stephensons had broken out on a higher plane. The cross which Christ had asked him to bear was of human workmanship.

"There you are," said the old priest sadly, opening his hands in a double gesture and slightly bowing his head. "It is a trashy little story not worth the telling but, if one adds up the pain, the frustration, the upset to many people, one sees why Our Lord was for ever warning the Apostles about this sin. Lie on the floor, you old mystic, but watch your step when you are standing up again."

Margery saw the Canon to the door. "Poor old man," she said, almost in tears. "It must have happened a long time ago but he is still sore about it now. He loved that little chapel, you can tell. Funny to think that he was a curate once."

I agreed but with secret reservations; certainly the Canon was once a curate but I am willing to bet that at the time of the story, he was a parish priest. Anyway, the lesson is both powerful and unexpected: the yardstick to measure both prayer and neurosis is, too often, jealousy.

6

OUR MR PONSONBY

Does God ever smile? True, there are few mentions of His mirth in the Sacred Scriptures but could He invite us to call Him Father if He lacked that most winning of all gifts which He has given to His sons? A man without a sense of humour is to be avoided and a God who is not amused by the antics of His children could scarcely be the Father of a happy home.

Prayer in Church must be solemn, save for an occasional frolic on the organ or a gorgeous medieval gargoyle which gives such joy to the angels of God. Prayer in the bathroom and bedroom must presume a corresponding sympathy in God. Irreverence is a wholly different matter but this impudence is rarely found at the centre of any human heart.

Take it for granted that God shares both our laughter and our tears. Nothing gives Him more pleasure than when we sinners are prepared to laugh at ourselves. Is there any human trait less becoming than self-pity, especially when it seeps through to the face? How we come to despise those self-righteous people who

dare not admit a weakness and who, in every crisis,
think only of themselves. One smiles at the story of
the Liverpool girl who, one day, was met at the door
by her father, pale and trembling, on her return from
work. His was the classical explanation : "Your mother
has fallen downstairs and it has not done me any
good."

Above all others we neurotics must at all costs laugh
at ourselves. Surely we are laughable enough with our
strange quirks, fears, scruples, apprehensions which
will never be eased while we bottle them up. How
many a nervous breakdown could have been easily
avoided had the panic on a lower level come to the
surface in a hearty laugh. Lovers of Thurber will recall with recurring glee the cartoon of two great bats
hanging above a man in a boiled shirt at a dinner table
with the lesson in the caption, "O Lord, here they are
again."

Mr Ponsonby's escapade is not inserted here to be
facetious and certainly there is no deep spiritual signi-
ficance in his tale. Yet he played an important part in
my education and may teach a lesson to neurotics
which is not to be found in St John of the Cross.

The charm of our Mr Ponsonby lay in this heaven-
sent ability to laugh at himself. He was otherwise not
very prepossessing, with his nervous little giggle,
moist eyes and timid gait. Visitors to the office hardly
noticed him while his colleagues, before they knew
him, had to take a firm grip on themselves. Our Mr
Ponsonby was cool and efficient only with a ledger

before him and a pen in his hand. In most other positions he seemed permanently apprehensive while the habit of clearing his throat every two minutes wrought havoc with the junior staff. When he retired, he looked quite young for sixty; they tell me that he looked old for sixty when he was still in the sixth form at school.

Mr Ponsonby worked under me for many years without consciously disclosing his charm. It took years to probe beyond the nervous giggle, to sift the clues which led to a gallant personality hidden behind a tedious little cough. Thus, many years before, I had been surprised to see him eating his four neat sandwiches at lunch time, with, propped up before him, a copy of *The Connoisseur*. One came, after a time, to note the beautiful leather of his wallet and briefcase and the way in which he fondled this before putting them away. Once, in an exceptional moment of confidence, he spoke to me about music, comparing the influences which moulded Liszt and Chopin in a brilliant and very original way. Our Mr Ponsonby was a cultured man but he was also very frightened and his struggle to master a nervous temperament lasted many years. One of the clerks once found on his desk a pamphlet entitled: "How to Hold Your Own in Public," while another claimed to have overheard a mumbled imprecation, "Lord, why did you make me such a silly fool?" This last quickly became an office slogan and Ponsonby would always answer with his nervous giggle, "I fear that it is only too true."

Our Mr Ponsonby was the victim of many phobias,

high on the list of which was a morbid dislike of dogs. The office boy found it out after stalking him from Holborn Station and Ponsonby, when challenged, made no secret of the fact. Indeed he confessed quite simply that this was the reason why he always had a stick. Further, he could explain his dread, a quaint survival from a fright in early youth. Apparently the young Ponsonby, running slightly ahead of his devoted mother, was challenged on Chiswick Bridge by an ill-natured pug. "I was never attacked," he observed in his precise manner. "But the pug just sat before me for twenty minutes thinking savage thoughts. My mother shouted 'Harold, stand very still' but, d'you know, I hardly needed such advice. I pulled friendly faces and made soothing noises but the pug was hard by nature and very slow to respond. I am pleased to say that it later bit a policeman so its grudge was with life in general and not just personal to me."

Young Ponsonby never forgot Chiswick Bridge. A fear which began with pugs later spread to Alsatians and eventually embraced dogs of every species, even poodles and those little sausages on wheels. "The fact is, Dawes," he would say, "dogs do not like me and I can hardly blame them for that. When I turn a corner, I see them winking to one another and signalling to friends further down the street. They stare as I pass them and many a time I have seen their noses twitch. There have been times when I have crossed the road to dodge them and once, in shame, I actually retraced my steps. I am a rational being and I find it very frustrating that one cannot reason with a dog. If only I could explain to them that I am a mild and modest fellow, I feel sure that they would leave me alone."

Everybody in the office knew of this aversion to dogs. Ponsonby would receive dogs on his Christmas cards and press cuttings of men and women who had been bitten in his letter tray. Our Mr Ponsonby was not unduly worried about the chaffing and often provided new material himself.

I remember very well his vivid account of an appalling week-end spent with his married sister down near Sevenoaks. He discovered too late that his brother-in-law had bought a black, maladjusted mongrel with a vertical take-off and retractable legs. To make things worse, this brother-in-law had spent many happy evenings adding to its natural repertoire of tricks. It could now leap as high as a screen, open a door, knock food off the table and even stub a lighted cigarette. Ponsonby spent a restless Saturday evening in a ring-side seat. At one moment, Aldwyn, the dog, was on his lap with its jaw held open so that his brother-in-law could display its teeth. Once, when he was persuaded to take it for a walk, he abandoned it near the station, took a bus back to his sister and left it to fend for itself. On the Sunday while his sister was at church, our Mr Ponsonby was forced to lock himself in the bathroom while Aldwyn used the rest of the house to rehearse his tricks.

It was this brother-in-law who first proposed to poor Ponsonby that he ought to acquire a dog for himself.

He pointed out that this morbid fear of dogs was completely neurotic and could so easily be cured. He sketched out a rosy picture of our Harold, free for ever of such childish apprehensions, striding across Hampstead Heath with two whippets at his heel. "Buy a puppy of your own," he cried, "and in two months you will hardly know yourself." Ponsonby, for different reasons, was prepared to accept the truth of this.

The office cheered excitedly when Harold Ponsonby proposed his plan. Secretaries rushed out for samples of dog meat and dog biscuits while one enterprising accountant put through an emergency call to the vet. Ponsonby was a little flustered but I found him reading a pamphlet, "How to save your pal from rabies," during lunch. "I do not really like the idea of getting a dog," he admitted sadly, "but we have a duty as rational beings to master our fears. They tell me that if I overcome this dread of dogs, I may cure myself of other worries too. Besides I am unmarried, living quietly with my mother, and a dog might bring a little brightness into her life. At least she is willing to care for it while I am at the office; if I do not like it, I need only see it at week-ends." I encouraged Ponsonby in his resolution; to laugh at oneself and to face one's panics is a corollary to lying on the floor.

After a month of indecision the puppy finally arrived. I saw it only in snapshots and in the merry twinkle which brightened its master's normally listless eyes. Ponsonby still carried a stick but he held himself straighter and answered questions about it with a certain pride. He, once or twice, called it "that little blighter" and would pop out at lunch to buy a lead, a special brand of biscuits and a comb. The office boy said that he also purchased a new pair of bedroom slippers; if so, our Harold kept this secret to himself. As to its name, Ponsonby rejected many bright suggestions, among them Bertrand Russell to encourage the puppy to sit down in the street.

He toyed with Chopin and Shakespeare and finally, as a tribute to the immortal Trollope, named it Proudie after the Bishop of Barchester.

Six months after his adoption, Proudie showed signs of growing very big. He was partly Airedale but with unusual features which only his mother and father could explain. When I questioned Ponsonby about its size, he seemed slightly embarrassed. "It isn't as though I like any size of dog," he replied with a titter, "and as I only bought Proudie to cure my apprehensions, I thought I might as well have one big enough to be frightened about."

Just a year after Proudie's arrival, our Mr Ponsonby announced his engagement to be married and, in the office, there was junketing on every side. As always, he bore the teasing with resignation for he was obviously very happy and proud. It was noticeable that he supplied few details and never explained how this sudden alliance came about. All that we could discover came in answer to a question: "Yes, we will be keeping Proudie, my future wife is very fond of dogs."

He said little in public but, as he was in secret seething, the whole story eventually had to come out. He described in his modest, punctilious style the strangest courtship ever known to me. Ponsonby was led to the altar by his dog. For, on the Saturday afternoon in question, when he took Proudie to the Heath for an airing, marriage was very, very far from his mind. He admitted that he was far more afraid of women than of dogs. He loved Proudie but thought him sufficient commitment for one timid man.

Ponsonby lugged him along on a lead, loosed him, whistled him back, ran half a mile to catch him, stood with a superior smirk on his face while Proudie jumped and frolicked near the trees. Ponsonby talked to Proudie as they paced the Heath together and though the dog said nothing, Ponsonby saw in his eye a glint of genial agreement when his master admitted in secret that he was a silly fool.

Then our Harold had the thought that he would drop in for confession to save himself another journey later on. The church was near the Heath and as Ponsonby led a simple life with few digressions, the dog would not have to wait outside for long. As he tied Proudie to the presbytery railing, Ponsonby gave him a modest pat, two lumps of sugar, a pious thought or two for meditation and a more general recommendation to be good.

Ponsonby now admits that he was never good at knots. He thought that Proudie was safely tied but no sooner ·had he joined the confession queue and signed himself devoutly than the peace of Hampstead and Hendon boroughs was shattered in a trice. Ponsonby heard such a penetrating shriek that he automatically looked towards the tribune to see if the parish choir was practising. Two further howls in quick succession convinced him that this was worse than the Missa De Angelis. Much as he loved his puppy, he remained for a moment glued to his pew. Would his new found courage stretch as far as this? He only went out because the other penitents were staring in his direction and he feared that the priest might pop his head out to excommunicate him there and then. He grabbed his stick, took Holy Water liberally in case he should meet the devil and emerged, looking a little like Proudie, with one of his gloves carried between his teeth.

The worst had happened. Not only was Proudie loose but he was standing, legs akimbo, impeding the passage of an enormous dog. For a moment Ponsonby thought that it was a miniature camel but he quickly pulled himself together and changed his mind. Both dogs had their engines running and were revving up. And behind the brutal monster was an ineffectual little woman, shrieking hysterically what sounded very much like abuse.

Ponsonby was, later, very sorry for what he did. He admitted that, in the heat of the moment, he lost all control. Yelling at Proudie as far as the glove in his mouth would permit and raising his stick in self-protection, he loosed a tremendous kick.

The dogs, seeing the raised stick, thought that they were under starter's orders and the kick was the sign to go. Proudie and the miniature camel gave a double yelp of satisfaction and bounded down the road. Proudie's lead, trailing behind him, proved no handicap. In a matter of seconds they were round the corner and only the sound of blue murder in the distance told Ponsonby that the battle had commenced.

Our Mr Ponsonby stood stunned for a moment with the glove in his mouth and his stick above his head. All that he had always dreaded had now happened, he was about to be involved in a dog fight, his cowardice would be proclaimed in public in the very middle of Hampstead Heath. He did what he had never done in his life before, he rounded on the hapless woman and said with mounting fury, "Madam, can't you control your blasted dog."

Apparently the woman was too far gone to heed his wrath. She sat on a stone by the side of the church and fanned herself. Our Harold felt powerless to help her, as he told me later; with Proudie he knew how to pat and comb, how to fix the lead to his collar; a woman in such distress would hardly welcome attentions like these. He could but stand stupidly, listening to the sad lament beside him, "I should have known, I should have known that he would never listen to me. I am afraid of him really; I am much too timid for a great big dog like that."

Ponsonby did not propose at once. He was too shaken, too worried, too ashamed of his cowardly behaviour to risk another sacrament that afternoon. He could only apologise for his heated words, only console her, explaining, as so often in the office, that he was terrified of dogs. She smiled again. When she asked what they should do, Ponsonby assumed the stance of Napoleon to reassure her: "Do?" he said with superb contempt. "We'll do absolutely nothing; let them eat themselves!"

She gladly agreed and as she, too, had come that way to seek confession, Ponsonby stepped aside and with a little bow let her lead the way into church. So they knelt in the confession queue together, each with one anxious ear cocked towards the Heath. God must have smiled as, for the first time in his life, our Mr Ponsonby confessed having lost his temper; he told me that he had also made a mental note to consult the experts for he was not certain if "blasted", shouted in such sacred precincts, was a sin.

Four penitents went home that day for, when confession was over, they found Proudie and the miniature camel making a firm purpose of amendment outside the church.

And once, years later, when I called to see our Harold, Mrs Ponsonby said how sad he would be to have missed me. "He is out on the Heath somewhere," she added smiling, "teaching Proudie a new trick."

7

CELIA'S ENGAGEMENT

Ours, I suppose, was a good Catholic home. We certainly had fish on Fridays, the definitive sign for the average Englishman of those who have sold their souls to Rome. In fact, we went much further than fish. If all our prayerbooks had been placed head to tail, they would have stretched to Jerusalem, while the statuary in our combined bedrooms gave us a status second only to Madame Tussaud's.

With only one crucifix and a solitary prayerbook, I was judged by the children to be very Low Church. Margery boasted a brace of miraculous Madonnas, a portrait of Christ painted in ecstasy by a Portuguese sister, a candle carried by Pope Leo XIII on some famous occasion and a reliquary which would have made Chaucer smile. The children took after their mother in piety if not in taste. Their statues were luminous and plastic, of a style often associated with souvenir shops on the Margate esplanade. They loved these garish reproductions and I doubt if Our Lady is fussy about art. Despite the ecclesiastical bric-abrac in the bedrooms I used, at one time, to worry about our faith. Lying on the floor each day, absorbed in the mystery of the Divine Presence, I wondered how I could teach my children to pray. The practice of the presence of God seemed so essential that I would have loved to have had them all lying on their backs.

Margery scotched the suggestion with an unkind reference to poor Mr Owles. The Canon blanched when I asked him and, though he wrapped up his answer in polite, theological jargon, he made it very clear that my methods were too odd. Fr Mulligatawny, the curate, was hot on the family rosary; he begged me not to worry so much about the mystery of the Trinity but to entrust my family daily to the great Mother of God. Miss Copsley-Smith, dispensing enormous gins, thought that every soul must find its own level and that a little casual agnosticism never did a teenager any harm. Lastly, the Little Nun wrote to say that piety was family feeling towards God. She was quite certain that my children had it and that on no account should it be artificially produced.

Contemplation was, therefore, off and, in its place, we tried the family rosary without much success. The telephone intervened three times in four decades and in the muddle I forgot the title of the fifth. There was general giggling and the boys sent my name to the Catholic Enquiry Centre for a postal course. So ended my efforts to make my family godly; with some sorrow we reverted to laissez-faire.

In so many devout books written for Christian parents, authors take it for granted that Mum or Dad gather the children round them for a heart to heart talk. This never happened or looked like happening in our home. Once the children had gone to boarding school, Margery and I were forced into the background and rarely dared to assert our views in matters of faith. Either Fr X or Mother St Y were quoted against us and we found ourselves under instruction from the boys. Margery, bolder than I and convent-trained, might occasionally deliver a talk on Christian behaviour but the children would laugh and call out for silence "as Mummy is going to give a homily!" I kept myself to myself. Margery said that I had let her down, that I was ashamed to profess my faith before my children and she even employed the "let us ask Daddy" technique. It was safer not to speak. I could manage a factual discussion on the number of Cardinals in the Roman curia but, when it came to purity, confession or communion, a painful embarrassment settled on us all. These cosy chats set out so sympathetically in the pamphlets proved hopelessly out of place in our blasphemous house. Should one feel so awkward in speaking to one's children about the dearest and most important facts of life? I used to lie on the floor and pray for an enlightenment which was never granted; shyness triumphed on either side.

The children were unreliable but never bad. We used to have a liturgical spell with Dominus Vobiscums ringing round the bathroom as Harry and

Benjamin practised for High Mass. After playing
priests day and night for a week, the liturgy was dis-
carded and God gave way to the Australian cricket
tour. On one vacation, Celia went all godly after a
term in Mother Mary of the Holy Trinity's class. Celia
spoke in a religious whisper and, when asked what was
the matter by her mother, announced that she was
making reparation for the sins of the world. She was
going to be nun at the time but, by the next vacation,
her very soul would swoon for jazz. Elvis Presley, or
whoever it was, dislodged St Aloysius and the nearest
that we came to contemplation was a recording of
Bing Crosby singing "Bless This House". My only
chance of speaking about religion was when the boys
were short of cash. They would have borne long ex-
tracts from *The Ascent of Mount Carmel* to get half-
a-crown. If piety is family feeling towards God, I
could cease from worry; they treated God much as
they treated Margery and me.

There were the usual difficulties. At one time Harry
ran up debts in secret, Benjamin turned secretive,
Celia sprawled in a sofa reading romantic magazines.
Or they would tease Betty, their little sister, and she
would run to me. Celia at sixteen was crazy about
dancing and some of the dances to which she was invited seemed to Margery very advanced. Celia
informed me of one such dance that Mother Mary of
the Trinity approved entirely and that all the proceeds
were to go to a leper colony outside Singapore. If
the end could justify the means in such exalted circles,

Margery and I could only shut our eyes and pray. We prayed for the children every day but, save for fish on Fridays, could do little else.

In due course the boys left school for university and three years later Celia was an undergraduate reading botany with infectious zest. She was now the image of her mother as I had known her twenty-five years before. This physical bond proved often irresistible and from the age of sixteen onwards Celia, more than any of the others, made our home. She was motherly to me, endlessly patient, always sympathetic; we shared a love of poetry and music and a lively interest in little people, their foibles, heart-breaks, hobbies, attitudes to life. She would bounce into the drawing-room, laughing, to tell me of the secondhand car that some friends were buying, of the lecturer's poodle who yawned during his master's lecture, of a Parsee graduate who had proposed to her. She was very pretty, refreshingly happy, industrious and kind. Our daily routine went on peacefully without her but her comings and goings, her friends, her rags, her dresses, dances and expeditions set the interest and pattern for our lives.

Celia had been at the University for two years and seemed deeply committed when Margery informed me tearfully that our daughter wanted to become a nun. The girl had not said this in so many words but, when Margery was pressing for information about her boy friends, Celia's non-committal answers had served as a warning and a clue. Margery could only hope that she was wrong, she advised me not to say anything about it, she begged me to mark her words.

I could not help smiling for while Margery and I in the olden days had often discussed the unlikely honour of a priest or nun in our family, we had never wanted God to take this too seriously. The quest for a suitable husband for her daughter lies at the centre of a mother's thoughts. Margery had never said so, but I knew very well that she saw in Celia's future marriage the prolongation of her own maternal life.

To me even the hint of a possible vocation to religion came as a sickening shock. According to all the holy books, I should have greeted the news with a heartfelt Alleluja for can there be a higher favour than this? Yet doubts pressed in on every side and mounted until I felt both resentful and rebellious towards God. It became increasingly hard to lie on the floor, more and more difficult to submit to God as a father, less and less certain whether I believed in His existence at all. In public no hint was given, but I found myself watching Celia with pain and incredulity, wondering how a girl so affectionate could plot in secret to dash all her parents' hopes.

Why was I so distressed? I had to recognise the fact that Celia at twenty-one could do what she wished with her life. I could not stop her from being a nun any more than I could prevent her from marrying a Parsee if she wished to or of living in San Francisco should she so choose. I would, one day, lose her anyway. On the other hand, if she entered a convent we

would have to visit her and sit in a gloomy parlour;
she would never enter her home again. They would
dress my Celia up in linen blinkers and pick for her,
out of the litany of saints, some high-falutin' name. A
further, more painful doubt assailed me as to whether
priests and nuns were so much better than men and
women working in the world? I must not weary you
with my morbid misgivings all of which seem so ridiculous now. Behind all these bitter thoughts lay a far
more terrifying problem, was I so sure that there was
a God? Lying on the floor, striving for peace, adoring
God as a step to sanity, were these sufficient proofs of
His existence, arguments strong enough for me to
allow my beloved daughter to waste her life? Ours
may not have been a very edifying home, but Celia's
vocation was surely based on my behaviour over so
many years. She believed in God and her faith was un-
troubled because mine had seemed so secure.

It is never easy to obtain advice on so personal a
subject for there would be special pleading on either
side. The Canon was ex officio prejudiced in favour
of vocations while Fr Mulligatawny already had three
sisters nuns. On the other side, most of my friends,
even the Catholics, would condemn such a stultifying
step. Nuns are only fashionable in Britain when they
quit their cloister for the world. My friends would
agree that God is all very well in heaven, but it is
carrying belief a little too far when a pretty girl
squanders her life for Him. Margery herself would
not put it this way but if I had doubts about it, I could

presume a similar state of misgiving even in her.

In the end and with considerable hesitation I decided not to look for advice. Instead, I turned up the passage of Genesis to read about Abraham and Isaac for it dawned on me that this ancient patriarch, far out in the desert, faced a similar issue to myself. It was an effort to lie on the floor. Here indeed was a test; in cold blood and with every personal interest pulling against it, to make an act of faith. Leaving Celia's decision aside, for she was in this her own master, was I prepared to accept her departure for the sake of a God who had come to me, lying on the ground? Here was a heart-rending choice between the absorbing physical love of my own daughter and an intangible awe towards a being, always invisible, who meant nothing physical to me at all.

Well, Celia went to her convent. She finished her degree with a glorious burst, sparkled with love for us both in what I knew was her last summer holiday with us and then told me as we paced the sand dunes outside Burnham that she thought that she would like to be a nun. The shyness of former days remained. We said very little to each other, we agreed in a general way that this was a very great honour, that we would miss each other very much. I took it as a compliment when Margery later told me in tears that I was heartless and that even Celia had been astonished that I seemed so genuinely pleased.

"Pleased" is too slight a word. Is there any word in any language to express the relief after a cold-blooded act of faith? I had felt, lying on the floor, that friendship grows painful and embarrassing with all the giving from one side. Celia was not mine to give—doubtless she would have gone without me—but I shared with Abraham the supreme satisfaction that consent was mine. God could never mean to me as much as did Celia but, in one glorious moment, I was determined to show that I loved Him more.

Celia is very happy in her convent and, maybe, part of her strange contentment stems from an act of surrender similar to mine. Hers, I think, was the easier part for she now has a multitude of schemes, exhibitions, offices, employments, a lovely black habit to help her feel holy and a monster rosary clanking by her side. She tells me that it often reminds her of our famous family rosary which ended in gales of laughter so many years ago.

Margery is, now, very proud and moves with the majesty of a Reverend Mother; I, too, am contented to have it so. But the God who fills the heavens and will one day reward us, is still not able to fill Celia's empty room.

8

TO HEAVEN WITH BUZZ

It would be strange to write a handbook for neurotics without any reference to sex. The two are invariably linked. Neurosis in older people is frequently attributed to sexual vagaries, while adolescents live in terror of going mad. Children are often frightened by well-meaning teachers who, to drive home a salutary lesson, tamper with the facts. A world famous neurologist, well known to the Canon, publicly asserted that the cause of most neurosis is not sexual misbehaviour but a sense of guilt. Only those risk neurosis in sexual, as in other actions, who deliberately do what they know to be wrong. This famous neurologist originally came from Cork.

Sex has been made more difficult for men and women of my generation by the social and moral revolution which has rocked our world. Our parents were raised on nineteenth-century standards, Can-Can, Little Lord Fauntleroy and the pre-Raphaelite school. Those were the days when Anthony Trollope could spend two enthralling chapters preparing for

Johnny Eames and Emily Dale to kiss. In fact they may never have come to this for my memory is faulty and I may have drawn my lovers from two different books. Our parents, children of this righteous age, could but pass their standards on to us. Why, my own poor mother at the age of ten was all but expelled from a convent school in Holland because she announced at breakfast that she could tell the size of her future family by counting the wrinkles on her wrist.

Our generation enjoyed more freedom but only at a price. We were forced to be frauds. The people around us adopted new manners which a false conscience told us were impure. Girls wore short skirts as the fashion demanded but they felt, or were told, that Our Lady would not like it and that they were doing very wrong. So Margery as a little girl was taken to the movies but, for the sake of Jesus, Mary and Joseph, had to close her eyes during any kissing scene. Her mother, like a foreman ganger, blew on a little whistle if danger lay ahead. Once, Margery opened one eye ever so little and was promptly caught. She still nurses a grievance for though she had seen nothing but her own eye lashes, she was rushed to the presbytery to tell the priest. Did we boys fare better? Angelic virtue was the standard held before us; I grasped, too late to make a fuss about it, that angels, lacking bodies, know nothing of sex.

To-day, of course, everything is different and Celia at fourteen was studying biology and taking a plastic model of a rabbit's innards to bed. I smiled piously when I was told that Mother Mary of the Holy Trinity —surely with such a name above suspicion—had given her six lectures on the love life of the garden worm. Harry at seventeen was all set to instruct us both on fallopian pregnancies. I feared to repress him; it was his mother who said, "Later, darling, that is hardly a suitable subject for meals."

This was never intended as a book for adolescents; the problems of puberty are treated at length in many learned manuals and are printed indelibly in many hearts. Looking back, one may trace the errors made by so many people which later led to scruples and to a lasting sense of guilt. I am not here referring to actual sin. A cold-blooded act of impurity leaves little room for doubt. It is the vague apprehension about nebulous acts, half-confessed, half-committed, which raises a crop of worries later on.

The sixth and ninth commandments carry some of the characteristics of the Highway Code. Driving offences are frightening in this respect that a law abiding citizen who would never break a law or fall foul of the police on any other subject may, of a sudden, find himself a criminal on bail. In much the same way, men and women who would never forge or steal or wrong their neighbour, may wake up one morning in a state of grievous sin. Only a clear judgment, precise knowledge and a robust and cheerful outlook will rid us of this irrational anxiety and doubt. I, once, had the folly and good luck to leave the communion rails in a panic while the priest was at the other end of the line. Feeling that I would certainly be damned if I received communion unshriven and spotting an old priest at the back of the church reciting his breviary, I sought confession just to be on the safe side. He was a wise old man and must have witnessed my contortions. He said very firmly, "No, go back to communion first." Obediently I retraced my steps and have never been troubled since.

It would be a mistake to devote much space to such morbid topics when sex itself plays such a noble and vital part in our happiness. Would it, then, be sufficient to pause long enough on the standard worries which trouble so many about sex? In this matter, more than in any other, each individual thinks that he or she is odd. Each regards lustful thoughts and desires, homosexual urges, impure dreams and nocturnal disturbance as an affliction peculiar to himself. Sane on every other subject, each believes in secret that he or she is going mad. Thousands imagine that they are perverts on the evidence of irrational dreams. Sanity comes when one can persuade oneself, anything to the contrary notwithstanding, that one is no more crazy than anyone else. This is a plain fact. Presume oneself normal until outside evidence proves the opposite.

Again, there is a perpetual fear among young people that the sexual faculty will atrophy unless frequently pondered and satisfied. Another distinguished doctor, a psychologist, has pointed out recently that nature works exactly the other way round. This expert compares sexual capacity to a deposit in the bank. You put your money in your account and then forget all about it; it will be waiting for you when you require it at any time. The more you worry about sex, the more you take it out and stimulate it, the quicker it will evaporate. This psychologist deplored the tragic fact that many young people in the middle twenties are hardly capable of happy marriage, not because they did not use their sexual powers but because they have thought so much about them that they turned stone cold.

How many foolish fantasies about this subject are conjured up. There are those who look back and try to re-examine, at the age of forty, acts which they committed at fifteen. It is wholly impossible to assess past guilt on such a subject and we do far better to make an act of sorrow in the present moment than to unhinge ourselves with worry about the past.

Others look forward and persuade themselves that sex is a young man's burden which they will grow out of in middle age. We never do. A famous old priest once said that he was now far too old to foretell the future but that the most difficult time that he experienced in a life-time was from eighty to eighty-five.

Finally there are those who, in ignorance or guilt, have acquired habits which they hope to break in a moment by a sudden act of will. Such a lightning change is sometimes achieved but it is not normal; a habit as strong as smoking is not easily broken without a struggle over many months and years. Given the assistance of grace, there are often sudden conversions, but it is better to be prepared for a long struggle than to surrender in disappointment to despair. On this, more than on any other subject, the Fatherhood of God is all important for He who gave us the gift of sex understands its working and will surely make allowances with those who are sincere. Besides, it is so sad to make purity into a negative, anxious disposition when it should be the most virile, positive department of our lives.

So much has been written about this subject that I must be forgiven for treating of these worries here. Far more important than a negative approach is the forward view of life's most lovely virtue and for this I found no more helpful guide than Buzz.

I was crossing to the United States for a second round of lectures and Buzz joined the Mauretania at Le Havre. Only the United States could produce a guy like Buzz, crew cut and husky, with the chassis of the Orang-Outang and the eyes of a bottle-fed calf.

Those like myself, who had sailed from Southampton, could look down with a tolerant condescension on the crowd of would-be passengers herded on to the quay at Le Havre. I gazed with horror and compassion at the mob of American tourists, yapping and snapping, trying to take just one last picture or to dispose of unwanted francs. I could see a turban or two, a Messiah or two, a huddle of nuns, two prosperous priests with cigars and breviaries and a jostle of ordinary tourists as excited as children at the zoo.

They all looked much the same with their cameras, gum, souvenirs, deodorants, vitamin tablets neatly packed away in those Pan American grips. They all looked the same except for Buzz, a lone traveller, head and shoulders taller than his neighbours and standing out a mile.

I spotted him again in the saloon at dinner but we first spoke in the library after early morning Mass. One of the prosperous American priests was at the altar and Buzz was serving with an unselfconscious piety, so rarely seen in the British Isles. I, being English, had wedged myself into a corner behind a walnut table, piously hoping that no one would disturb me at my prayers. As soon as Mass was finished, Buzz came over with a frown on his normally placid brow.

He look so worried that I feared that he must have lost $1,000 or be trying to escape from the police. "Say," he began loudly, "do you know what the September intention for the Apostleship of Prayer is? I haven't gotten my leaflet yet and, when I asked in Rome and Venice, they just looked puzzled, as if they thought I was nuts."

Alas, I, too, looked puzzled ; the Apostleship of Prayer was new to me. "O.K.," said Buzz, calming me down with his hands, "I guess I'll just have to say the prayers; God'll kinda guess what it's all about."

Such a chance acquaintanceship, in the confined world of an ocean liner, blossoms into friendship very fast. I met Buzz many times that day in the drawing-room writing letters, in the lounge at a piano recital, in the purser's cabin for cocktails before lunch. He stood on no form, expected no introduction, nursed no shyness, talked as the mood moved him about anything. You rarely meet such openness outside the United States. There may be unpleasant Americans but, if I met any, the memory has been speedily erased by the unspoilt friendliness of Buzz.

We paced the deck together and pored over hundreds of coloured snapshots, mainly of American tourists, behind the Parthenon, before the Coliseum, beside the Pope. Buzz explained that these had been taken mainly for Rosemary Anne. Next, I saw Rosemary Anne herself, back home in Ohio, standing by the Rambler, sitting at a barbecue, kneeling on a prie-dieu before a flower-decked shrine. "Those were our solemn espousals," said Buzz with pride, "we plan to be wed before Christmas; you can't quite see the Reverend Louis J. Flaherty of Immaculata College, he was too much to the left."

The Reverend Louis J. Flaherty meant much to Buzz. Father said this, that and the other; Father advised on the furniture for the future chalet; Father was going to put Junior's name down for Immaculata on the very day of his birth. Father Louis J. Flaherty it was, who had instructed Buzz and Rosemary Anne about marriage and had given them a philosophy which would carry them happily through life. Buzz, like many other American boys of his age, spoke with all the authority of a text-book, heavy print for beginners, small type for those in their second year. He was both intelligent and simple, amply satisfied that he knew as much as he needed to know.

The Reverend Louis J. Flaherty, like so many other American priests, drew his parables from the ups and downs of everyday American life. Where we in Europe tend to fall back on Cardinal Newman and the fathers of the desert, the Reverend Louis J. Flaherty had been to Cape Canaveral for his views on married life. At first it sounded to me very slick and scientific; now, looking back, it seems amazingly apt. I studied Arts and am poorly versed in scientific technicalities, Buzz, who was majoring in science, could explain the details both to me and to his precious Rosemary Anne.

Love for Buzz was like a space journey with the heavens for a goal. This by itself was an improvement on so many modern similes which rarely get further than the bedroom door. The Space Ship is launched by a high-powered booster rocket which sets it on its journey but gives over when the jets in the space ship take control. So it whizzes ahead for thousands of miles until the second motor is exhausted and the little capsule, no longer drawn by gravity earthwards, flies alone to its destination, attracted by the power of the moon.

Buzz set it all out clearly with obvious sincerity; one felt that he might arrive at the altar in a space suit on his wedding day. After presenting the general picture, he elaborated, turning the pages of a mental note-book inside his head. For Buzz, like the Reverend Louis J. Flaherty and other wise people, saw that

sexual attraction and the act of marriage are but
means to a further end. Here is a powerful rocket indeed but with one clear function which must produce
a further reaction if it is to be judged a success. Buzz
put it all very well and though he was limiting his parable to himself and Rosemary Anne and to other young
people on the edge of marriage, much of his wisdom
would apply to men and women in other conditions
and at almost any age. He made it very clear to me
that the gift of sex, sex appeal, sex attraction is not
just sited in the body but must affect the soul as well.
He saw as a poor shadow of the genuine union, one
which has merely physical pleasure as the end. He
reckoned that the scientists at Cape Canaveral would
be bitterly disappointed if the rocket failed to raise
the space ship and just developed immense heat on
the ground. Failure faced the scientists if the rocket
burned itself out. All the skill, all the expense, all the
intricate machinery would be rendered useless and
reduced to a smouldering shell. "I guess," said Buzz,
"that many kids of my generation will end as sexual
scrap."

It was then that Buzz produced his slogan, borrowed
no doubt from the Reverend Louis J. Flaherty, "Don't
base your sex on the pituitary gland." I may have got
it wrong, Buzz may have gotten it wrong, the Reverend
Louis J. Flaherty may have said "cerebellum" in place
of "pituitary" but the principle behind the slogan
stands out a mile. For Buzz was right when he went
on to explain that sex must not be based on pictures

but on persons, it must not be fed by phantasms and imagination but on respect, a growing affection, tenderness and love. Fondness and fondling are the signs of sex. In his own country, he saw the danger in the High School, where kids are kept excited by mental pictures stimulated by pornography. "Everything they read," he said, "everywhere they look, everywhere they go, every gramophone disc to which they listen plug these unhealthy stimulants. I guess that they'll just burn themselves out. Many of them are not really in love with the girls they go with, they have their dream life, their dream pictures and almost any girl will do." Buzz was deeply pained by all this. He saw a wonderful faculty being wrongly titivated by those who knew no better, who had never met the Reverend Louis J. Flaherty or grasped the true dignity of married life. "In too many cases," he said shaking his head wisely, "the launching rocket burns itself out."

But Buzz himself was in his space capsule or soon would be, off with the charming Rosemary Anne. It was amusing for me, a middle-aged married man with four strapping children, to hear a boy, so full of sincerity and right thinking, describe the change-over from sex appeal to genuine love. Buzz might rhyme genuine with Clementine but love was love on both sides of the Atlantic and I could not but feel very happy for Rosemary Anne. She was to have a husband whose love was not entirely based on bodily attraction, who craved for true companionship in the centre of his soul. For him the long journey through life would be made tolerable and fruitful only in the deep and lasting union between two persons, between two souls. To Margery and to me this might all sound slightly Hollywood and technicoloured but I knew that every word of it was true. Margery's age is still an official secret, mine at the time was fifty-one. We both feel old enough to be our own parents and yet the profounder peace of married love is for us greater than it ever was in our honeymoon years. As Buzz gave me advice borrowed from the Reverend Louis J. Flaherty, he also renewed my gratitude and hope. In return, I could tell him nothing; he and the Reverend Louis J. Flaherty, neither of them married, had it all taped and knew it all.

But Buzz went even further than this—no small achievement for a kid, not yet married—and he had the most far-reaching vision of his space journey with Rosemary Anne. He knew they would be journeying together in their capsule bound for God. Buzz had it all in his head. He looked as if he might even give the references in Exodus and Genesis to show that sex and love are but the shadow of the final union of the soul with God. Buzz even had God taped. He knew how much the infinite God liked to teach us by using human incidents to foreshadow deeper and supernatural truth. So the blood of the paschal lambs smeared on the Hebrew doorposts in ancient Egypt was but a feeble sign of the spiritual protection won by Christ's blood on Calvary. Cana and its miracle, he assured me, was not just an isolated kindness to a young married couple but also the foreshadowing of the change of the wine at Mass. He seemed pretty sure and we may guess his authority that the sexual intimacy which plays so large a part in life is not an end but a beginning and foreshadows the final rapture prepared for men by God. So clear was he of this that he even put in a word for those who do not marry and on Christ's authority make themselves eunuchs for the Kingdom of God.

It was strange to pace the deck far out in the Atlantic while a young American boy with the intonation of a Hollywood documentary spoke so simply and refreshingly of the mystical union with God. A space ship may not be the most poetic form of transport but there was certainly majesty in Buzz's view of the human soul, no longer earthbound, drawn by the gravity of God.

I lay on the floor of my cabin with the liner slithering beneath me, to ponder Buzz and his philosophy. He may not have guessed it but he had come near to solving the greatest of all problems which so many earnest people have to face. It is the problem of the Canticle of Canticles, shunned by the Canon, hinted at by St Teresa in her words about mystical union, intensified by the artist when he tried to paint the mystical marriage of St Catherine, eventually faced by everyone who relaxes and lies on the ground. Dare one use sexual phraseology to express the love between the created soul and God?

"Don't base your sex on the pituitary gland," said

Buzz in his slogan and I could see that love on any level is damaged where the union between persons is created and controlled by fantasy. There is no sex life in the world of spirit and we make nonsense of life's most profound liaison when we try to picture it But the cold fact is that the God who loves me is the God who, on the physical level, thought out that tenderness which we call sex.

If I had met Beethoven, I would have gazed with awe at the man who could create such harmony. Had I met Shakespeare, I would have stood spellbound before the genius who never spoke like Hamlet or loved like Juliet but who had carried Hamlet and Juliet in his head. When I meet God in prayer, I am in the presence of the author of the love between Margery and me.

The words "Our Father" go so much further than my love for Benjamin and Harry; no words or phantasms are needed to express the bond with the Eternal Lover who made the love between Buzz and Rosemary Anne.

Filled with such thoughts far out at sea, I sought Buzz after dinner but could only find one of the prosperous American priests.

"Good evening, Father," I said.

He advanced with cigar and breviary to greet me. "Louis J. Flaherty is the name; pleased to meet you," he said.

— 9 —

EXIT THE LITTLE NUN

OUR last meeting was almost as strange as our first. Then, she had held my arm in a lecture hall in Cheadle, now she was holding it in Euston Station at the far end of the old Central Hall. Before us was an ancient vehicle mounted on a dais; from the look of it, a primitive engine or Stephenson's first pram. The Little Nun was not much concerned with the history of British railways, she reserved her smile for the weary men and women champing in a neighbouring queue. "My dear Mr Dawes," she said, "how lucky I am to be a religious. My needs are anticipated and settled by phone."

Ten years did not seem to have changed her much. Perhaps she was a little smaller, a little more stout, a shade more wrinkled, but with the same kind smile and darting eyes. Few could have guessed her total deafness; vibrant, she was far too interested in the world around her to be shut off by any lack of sound. Such was her spirit that deafness became in her an endearing trait. I, for one, would not have loved her so much without it and she, exactly geared to God's omniscience, remained unflustered and content.

She sat, as ever, sideways, quite unaware of the din of Euston, her hand on my arm and her eyes on my lips. It was only our second meeting in a lifetime, the first meeting in ten years. She was, yet, able to ask after Margery by name, to speak about the children and to resume, for a few minutes, our first discussion about history books. Civilities completed, and the word doubled its meaning in the graciousness of her manner, we moved at once to God. He was as real to her as British Railways and she assumed no sombre tone and godly manner to speak of Him. Where Buzz, who was young, saw God waiting for him at the end of a space journey, the Little Nun had reached her destination and seemed to have Him on the platform by her side.

"Mr Dawes," she said, bowing slightly, "I am very happy indeed to see you looking so well. When last we met, ten years ago, you thought that you were heading for a breakdown so there can be no doubt about it that the prayer of relaxation has suited you. If I wore one, you would be a feather in my cap. You must, however, seek to advance more slowly and not try to hurry God too much. I sometimes suspect that you are still a mild Pelagian, imagining that success in prayer turns on yourself. That would be a most dangerous mistake. It leads both to pride and to exhaustion, leaving us limp for everything else. Go peacefully. Do you recall the admirable simile of St

Peter of Alcantara, the friend of St Teresa, who compares us at prayer with soldiers keeping guard outside the palace gates. If the King comes out we feel rewarded; if not, we are quite content to stand still."

She consulted a small piece of paper, cunningly hidden underneath the edge of her large, white gamp. "Yes," she said, nodding in approval, "you were quite right when you remarked in your last letter that you were trying to free your prayers from mental pictures, for such phantasms are often hurtful, especially when we are pondering the love of God. They have a purpose when we are studying the gospels or praying to the saints. Any number of holy people have praised the use of some mental reconstructions but, in dealing with the world of spirit, these prove very fatiguing and inaccurate. In my old age, I am beginning to wonder whether thought itself is so important in prayer. Perhaps we try to think too much."

I noticed with sorrow that the Little Nun was, indeed, much older; she would ask a question unwillingly, afraid that she would not catch the answer and would lose the thread. It seemed kinder not to attempt too many questions or answers so I fell back on nodding my head.

"I am so glad that you agree with me," she said, relieved. "In prayer we must not think too much. After all, even in this world, we only entertain thoughts about a friend when he is absent; we would scarcely want thoughts if he were sitting in the room. I am talking to you, not having thoughts about you now.

When the pagan poet wrote to his girl 'I would not have my thoughts of thee instead of thee', he was proposing a very useful line for us. Perhaps this should be your next step, Mr Dawes."

Euston is not normally associated with contemplation, and a locomotive let off a shriek of protest from a nearby shed. On the Little Nun the noise was wasted, sounding no more than a sweet zephyr in the trees. "Those who have ears to hear, let them hear," and I could but clap my hands to my head. The Little Nun looked round astonished, then guessing what had happened, she smiled. "Mr Dawes," she said softly, "there are a few compensations for being deaf."

I had reached this same conclusion myself. Euston Station is not the ideal setting for a talk on mystical prayer with a deaf nun. To the slight embarrassment of sitting with a nun at all was added the need to mouth each syllable with the accompanying grimaces which such an exercise is bound to produce. The locomotive with a few, gay, carefree tootles, made it almost impossible for me to hear myself speak. I found myself yelling to the astonishment of the queue beside me and to the evident distress of the Little Nun. "There is no need to raise your voice," she said, tapping her fingers, "just move your lips and I am able to follow very well."

Yes, there were problems, but her earnestness was so contagious and the joy of being again with her so satisfying that even Euston Station assumed a mystic glow. I was able, when the locomotive had completed its rehearsal, to ask how she managed to retain so much enthusiasm for her work. "I find," I said, "that it becomes increasingly hard to get excited about the trivialities of everyday life. If I were a free man, I think I would leave everything and live like a hermit in a cave."

The Little Nun was very startled at this. "Mr Dawes," she remarked, scrutinising my lips, "I hope that I have not heard you correctly for if I have, then you should stop praying on the floor. You are turning into a fakir and we will soon have you breathing deeply and sleeping contentedly on a bed of nails. Since the Incarnation, such behaviour would be very out of place. It would be most awkward for us if, while we had our heads in the clouds looking for a vision, we saw Christ passing, going the opposite way."

She raised a warning finger and moved it to and fro. "Mr Dawes," she said, "I am not at all happy about your recent observation; can it be that you are one of those who think of Christmas as a merry, children's feast? It is the most adult feast in human history. God so loved this world that He sent His son on earth, born of a woman, and in this lies the difference between fakirs and ourselves. This world was more important to Christ than heaven or, presumably, He would have left ill alone."

The Little Nun looked smiling round Euston Station; she must have been the only soul in Britain who could gaze on it with love. She greeted a passing porter who spontaneously raised his cap; she held out

her podgy hands to two small Jamaican children
whose mother was fighting a losing battle through a
small glass window with an unseen clerk. She only
stopped smiling when her eye fell on the station
clock.

"Mr Dawes," she said, "my companions will soon
be returning to collect me and if there are to be ten
years between our meetings, I doubt very much if we
will see each other again in this world. Please make no
possible mistake about it, this is the important world
while it lasts. Even the contemplative monks, men like
the Carthusians, would never save their souls if they
entered their silent convents for salvation's sake. They
live in silence and say many prayers for the world in
general, for you and me. If Our Lord decided to come
to Cheshire, He would not come to give me consolation and He certainly would not want me swooning
in adoration; He would be desperately concerned with
the welfare and happiness of my parents and children,
with their bodies as well as with their souls. True, once
in the Gospel story Mary did a little swooning while
Martha, her sister, rushed about to do twice the work.
I personally would not care to base much on that one
example for Christ Himself was so busy that He could
only pray at night."

She sat back for a moment, relaxed. She pursed her
lips as though planning her next sally and placed both
hands in her lap. Her rest did not last for long. "Mr
Dawes," she said suddenly, gripping my wrist again
and turning sideways, "when Mr Sheed called his book

Theoolgy and Sanity he hit upon a vital, psychological truth. There can be no lasting sanity without a decision about God. Nor can we remain sane for long without the next step of which I have been speaking, namely that God's only son became a man. There are thousands of religious lunatics who are taken to institutions singing Allelujas inside a well upholstered van. Religious mania is, perhaps, the most painful form of lunacy; we go mad over the very cure which should set us free. And I would say that most religious lunacy is caused by a wrong notion about Our Lord. People cannot accept the simple fact that Christ wanted us to find our holiness in the ordinary duties of daily life. They turn at once to the Apocalypse—a most dangerous book for the unstable;—they fasten on to the more threatening passages in the gospel, they love to dwell on hell fire and to foretell catastrophe.

"Why is it that they conveniently skip the thirty years at Nazareth, the humble scenes and people, the times when Christ sat down with ordinary, even wicked people for a meal? Even to the very end on Calvary, Christ remained completely balanced, never fanatical, never hysterical, never morbid, never unapproachable. How has so sane a man given rise to so many crazy parodies? At the centre of His heart, Christ had this profound understanding and love of His Father and such an inner peace precludes neurosis of any sort. You cannot love God and be neurotic for long. That is why we should judge ourselves as Christians not by texts and eccentricities, not by a multiplicity of odd devotions, but by the amount of sanity which we show before the world."

The Little Nun fumbled with her hands for a moment and from her multiple skirts produced a small gun-metal watch. This she checked with the station clock. "My companions," she said, "will be here shortly but as nuns are always at least fifteen minutes early, there should still be plenty of time." She replaced her watch and took my arm.

"Mr Dawes," she said—and I was amused to note how she now used my name at the start of each observation—"the more I ponder the question, the more sure I am that sanity and Christianity spring from consideration for our neighbours and not from thinking too much about God. Be united to Him by all means as Our Lord was, but after that, turn your mind right away from yourself.

"Broadly speaking, the more you think, the more you think about yourself. I would say that all scruples, fears, religious mania, melancholy, hatred and impurity are based on the inability to control our thoughts. This is the supreme form of self-centredness. The more you love God and copy Christ, the more you will stop yourself thinking about yourself.

"How I wish that instead of spending so much time on Catechism and Doctrine, we could spend a little more time with children showing them how to control their thoughts. This is not psychology, it is pure Christianity; only if I stop thinking, will my right hand not know what my left hand does."

The Little Nun slapped her lips in the manner I could so well remember from ten years before. She was certainly much older, much more exhausted, making a deliberate effort to keep going, no doubt because of her views on Christ and on this world. More weary, she was, also, more serene.

She smiled at me. "Mr. Dawes," she said, "when I say that we must not think of ourselves, you and so many other people apply this to behaviour as though Christ was merely asking us not to pamper ourselves too much. When we say, 'But, Mary, you ought to think of yourself,' we mean, 'Mary, you must put at least half the omelette in the warmer for your own supper, you must get the children to wash up for a change.' The phrase could mean that but I think that Our Lord was teaching a far deeper lesson for, if we are to forget ourselves in behaviour, we must start by forgetting ourselves in our very thoughts. Too many people spend too much time thinking and mooning about themselves: 'How am I feeling to-day; was I successful, did she like me; what's for dinner?'—and then they find it impossible in their actions to forget themselves. The task of charity is impossible unless, for Our Lord's sake, we control our thoughts.

"People say to me, 'Sister, I cannot get these thoughts out of my head,' and I weep for them, for there is no tyranny greater and more cruel than this. Or I say, 'Now, Mrs Myerscough, try not to think of it,' and Mrs Myerscough answers 'Sister, I have to, it is preying on my mind day and night.' How terrible!

Fancy letting a thought, like a rat, gnaw away at your very mind."

She looked round anxiously, for there was no sign of any companion as yet. I asked a porter and learned that there was still twenty minutes before the train would be in. I was doubly pleased because the Little Nun looked so happy at this news.

Nothing could distract her from her theme. She must have felt that this would be her last conversation with me and she was determined to drive home her point. As soon as I resumed my seat, she was reaching for my arm. "The great principle," she said, "is that our minds are so designed that they can only hold one thought at a time. If I may use an old-fashioned example—I myself am old and old-fashioned—our minds work like a magic lantern with one slide showing on the screen. Only one can be showing and there is often another ready at the side. So many people will push a thought away but they leave it in the offing and do not show another in its place. They say to themselves, 'I must not think of my toothache—I must not think of my toothache'—but, in fact, they are thinking of not thinking all the time. They make no effort to substitute another thought. They should put it back in the box of slides and find another, quick. How glorious the sense of freedom when one has learned how to dismiss a thought for good. Greater still the triumph when one gets to the point in the lantern lecture where none of the slides contains oneself. When Our Lord told us to deny ourselves, He, as a profound psychologist, must have first wanted us to deny ourselves our thoughts. Do not try it all at once, Mr Dawes, you look the impetuous sort."

The Little Nun chuckled to herself. "I have seen," she said, "so many amusing cases of this. I remember an old woman who could not bring herself to go to Holy Communion; she had heard voices and was sure that she would be damned. Our Lord must have chuckled for I had her going to communion reciting the Charge of the Light Brigade. 'But, Sister, isn't that irreverent?' she asked me; I had to answer 'Not half as irreverent as approaching communion thinking and worrying about yourself.' I remember, too, a foreign bishop who feared that he could not swallow and was driving himself mad. 'My Lord,' I said, 'far worse than making yourself mad, you are making yourself selfish; you spend the whole of High Mass preoccupied with yourself. The day may come when the words of the liturgy will force you to think of God but, at the moment, take some sensation which will take your mind off your throat. God made you out of nothing; He will well understand'. Well, eventually I had him sitting at his throne with mitre and crozier, picturing himself parachuting from an aeroplane. True, he was still thinking about himself but in not so self-pitying a way. He swallowed perfectly, but the assistant priests complained later that the bishop kept swaying his body from side to side."

There was still time, so when, at last, the two sisters came to collect the Little Nun, she laughed with them for a moment and then sent them ahead to get the places on the train.

"I must tell you, Mr Dawes," she said, "of the nervous old priest, racked with scruples for many years, who had thought of nothing but himself. He loved God and his neighbour, tried hard to pray and to work for others but had no control of his thoughts. Whatever he was doing, he applied everything to himself. He analysed his prayers, he added up his distractions, he worried whether he was getting on with people, he examined his conscience until he was, literally, blue in the face. The stupid part was that, for many years, such scrupulosity passed for virtue and was almost taught to him at the seminary. He was seventy when he came to me. He visited our Children's Hospital on some other subject and I treated him as I would a little child. Mind you, I first talked to him about Our Blessed Lord. I told him, as I have told you, that we start our lives thinking only of ourselves. Next, if we are lucky, we meet God and come to think both of God and of ourselves. The final step comes when, for God's sake, we cease to permit ourselves any thoughts about ourselves.

"He accepted all this in theory but, in practice, he was preoccupied with the conviction that he was going to faint during Mass. 'Father,' I said, 'for the Lord's sake never accept any symptom suggested by yourself. If somebody tells you that you have a boil on your neck, believe it if you like. If the Master of Ceremonies at Mass tells you that your head is

missing, then only may you look. Die at the altar—
what could be better?—but stop worrying about
home-made symptoms which are a form of selfishness.'

"Well, we decided that he would take his mind off
fainting by use of a London transport map. A
Londoner by birth, I made him recite the stations on
the Inner Circle, starting at Earls Court and going
East. He promised me that he would. Two months
later he wrote to say that he had kept his promise, that
he felt very guilty saying Sloane Square, Victoria, St
James' Park during the Lavabo but that it worked. He
hoped that God had a sense of humour and would
understand this underground liturgy. I answered that
Sloane Square was just as eloquent a prayer as Dominus Vobiscum if said on purpose by a full and trusting
heart.

"I saw him yesterday in London. He was very happy
and certainly made me laugh. He told me how, when
he was coming to the sacristy, last Sunday, he could
tell that the altar boys were playing the fool. They
stopped dead when they heard his footsteps and one
of them shouted 'Look out, here comes the Rector.'
There was silence for a moment while one of them
peeped out through the half-closed door. 'It's all
right,' he shouted, 'it's not the Rector; it's only old
Charing Cross.'

"Pray for me, dear Mr Dawes," said the Little Nun
as I left her at the barrier and she hurried to the train
without once looking back. Within a year, she was
dead.

She practised all that she preached and she died as she lived. Where others would have rested, the doctors decided that it would probably be better to leave her free to work till the end. I heard later that she lectured in the morning and entered hospital to die that same afternoon.

10

NURSE OVALTINE

AFTER telling you all about it, I have been flat on my back for the past month.

I was taken ill just five weeks ago. It happened suddenly and without any of that panic which most of us dread over so many years. I was typing at my desk. Came a suggestion of nausea which might have been no more than indigestion; as it did not pass, I lay down on my bed. Thus Margery found me when she returned from shopping; she gave me a nip of brandy and the doctor called before lunch. He advised me to lie very still. Rarely in all these years had I felt more peaceful or more satisfied. The Canon came to hear my confession and I was anointed without a tremor and without a prayer. Formal prayer is often impossible in sickness; in its place was the relief that trivialities were over and that this was the moment of truth. I was carried to the ambulance, a very small suitcase beside me, containing more than enough for my reduced needs.

The inconveniences of a heart attack are trashy

when set beside the kindness that it provokes. I could see with shame that charity means so little between equals standing on their own two feet. When you are lying on your back, helpless, the thoughtfulness of others takes on a supernatural glow. It was a special joy to receive a "Get Well Quickly" card from Cleveland, Ohio, signed by Buzz and Rosemary Anne.

Margery, of course, meant everything and was with me every day. Harry brought his wife and children, one of whom, God help him, is thought to be the living image of myself. Harry is now nearly thirty; it was a relief to lie back in the knowledge that we were changing places, that soon I would be dependent on him.

The doctors tell me that if I am careful, I should soon be perfectly fit. They push things into me and draw things out and whisper together behind a screen. Once I was shown a diagram of the heart with a pencilled arrow to mark the scene of the accident. They are not philosophers but physicians; "heart" to them is just an organ, for they lack the vision of Miss Copsley-Smith.

Nurses come in and out, looking for sister, looking for love, looking for the thermometer, looking for trouble and, in the case of Nurse Ovaltine, looking for God. They give me food, pillows, pills and bed-pans and none of the indignities of illness has proved a problem once one has made the great decision to give way.

That I managed to yield with grace to a reduced status is due entirely to Nurse Ovaltine. I gave her this name because she settled me down in the evening and, also, because she is small, spherical and sweet. She it was who told me the parable of the piece of gristle which, if you find it in the bacon at breakfast, you leave discreetly on the side of the plate. "Mr Dawes," she said, smiling down at me, "the healthiest of hearts runs on just such a piece of gristle so that even the strongest of human beings is not very safe. When you think of it, there is only a small piece of gristle between ourselves and heaven or hell. Your bit of gristle has got stuck for a moment but really it is not all that much more rickety than a heart that is running well."

I had time and enough to meditate on this piece of gristle, lying peacefully on my back all day. I think I was ready for Nurse Ovaltine's second premise by the time that she came on duty, late on the following night. "Mr Dawes," she said gently when I had asked her about it, "try your very best to live in the present moment where your heart beats are. It is very silly to live in the past and to worry about it, it really has no meaning now. You cannot change the past whatever you do. And it is even more silly to try to live in the future which does not exist at all. The past was once real, the future has no reality at all. And so many patients make themselves ill worrying about what may happen to them. The fact is, Mr Dawes, that life is only in the present for all of us. Only in the present have I free will, only in the present is it possible to be patient, resigned, sorry for my sins. When I once said this to a patient he said in a panic, 'Nurse, are you trying to tell me that I am dying?' and I answered laughing, 'Mr Bootham, I am trying to tell you how to live."

So I passed another peaceful day, living only in the present, save for a few illicit moments when I looked forward to seeing Nurse Ovaltine. What she had said, helped me so very greatly; I wished so much that I had grasped it many years ago. It took a coronary thrombosis to teach me the lesson of the piece of gristle and a little nurse from Stratford Broadway to show the way to a more abundant life. The lessons of the Canon and of the Abbé Delpierre, the theories of Miss Copsley-Smith doubled their meaning as I thought that jealousy, selfishness, fear, love, contrition exist only in the present where we and our heart beats are. The next injection, the next bed-pan, the next spell of sleeplessness, the next kindness were all important. I said to myself, "Henry, this is your life."

The mystery of Nurse Ovaltine was not yet over for, on the following night, when she came round late to arrange my pillows, she had a large Bible in her hands. And when all her other work was done, she sat sideways by my bed to share the bed-light and, in a nasal, cockney accent, read the story of Moses as a little boy.

Lying on my back, relaxed, I could see the rushes in the river, the baby in its wattle basket and the

Princess on her way to bathe. Nurse Ovaltine stumbled over the words in her excitement and hurried forward so as to prove her point. She skipped past the murder, Moses' flight, the fight by the well, the marriage with Jethro's daughter, to get him with his herds on the hill side by the burning bush.

I was there long before her, I knew so well what was coming, I could fall, in spirit, on my face like Moses before the greatest mystery in the world. Nurse Ovaltine was trembling with excitement; she had to use a finger to mark the place. In her voice was the note of wonder at a new discovery, the burning bush had come to Stratford Broadway, to a modern world of thrombosis and ovaltine.

"... and Moses said to God: 'Lo, I shall go to the children of Israel and say to them: The God of your fathers hath sent me to you. If they should say to me: What is his name? what shall I say to them?' God said to Moses: 'I am who I Am. Thus shalt thou say to the children of Israel: He who Is hath sent me to you.'

"Mr Dawes," she said, smiling at me, "d'yer see wot I mean?"